The Forgotten Spy
Part I

The Forgotten Spy
Part I

Kyle Kiyotsuka

Cover art by Tkay2 Design
ISBN: 978-1-7333360-0-0 (Paperback)
ISBN: 978-1-7333360-1-7 (e-book)
Library of Congress Control Number: 2019910580
Printed in the U.S.A.
First Printing: September 2019

Dedications

To my Grandpa, Kinjiro Kabazawa
Thank you for your story.
To my Mom, Amy.
Thank you for the suggestion of writing things out.
To Dondi Iannucci,
Thank you for restoring my faith in everything.
To Jessica 'Jess' Lindner,
Thank you for simply being your awesome self.

Acknowledgments

To my mother, a massive *mahalo* for loving me unconditionally, sticking with me and supporting me always. I know I am not the easiest person to get along with, and moody as hell, so thank you so much for having the patience with me and just sticking with me always. I love you mom, always, especially when I don't show it. I truly do.

To Hannah Hart, Justine, Jenna, and Breanne Ezarik, a massive *mahalo* to you all. You all have reinspired me to bring new life to old projects. I do hope this suffices for now until I meet you all in person, we have lots to talk about.

To Dondi Iannucci, a massive mahalo for restoring my faith in everything. You helped me when I was at a very low point.

To Mollie King, your song "Back To You" came out just when I needed it. Your lyrics reassured me that I was not alone and that gave me great comfort. I can never thank you enough.

To Jessica 'Jess' Lindner, a massive mahalo for giving me the niche that I searched for and had been missing for my entire life. I can never thank you enough. I want to tell you so much more, perhaps when I finally meet you in person.

To Trysen Kaneshige of Tkay2 Design, a very special mahalo for the rad cover art designs! You get 'em brah! Check him out on http://tkaytwodesign.com/ and on Instagram: @tkay2inspire_ and business Instagram: @inspiretocreatemedia

Contents

Introduction

Kinjiro Kabazawa is a forgotten American hero. He was a combat veteran who on the, frontlines, survived countless threats to his life. However, my grandfather at heart was a simple man. He had no need for fame or glory. Through all his amazing adventures, and hair-raising escapes, he always wanted nothing more than to return to his simple work at a dairy on Kaua'i in Hawaii.

When my grandpa told me stories of his service, I didn't write anything down. In keeping with the Hawaiian tradition of oral history, I memorized all his stories. I occasionally interrupted him but otherwise just let him talk. I did not dare to put his words on paper until my mother finally suggested that I write down his stories. Twelve years, one genre switch, one point-of-view switch, a billion drafts, millions of songs, and a revelation later, the result is in your hands.

Grandpa told me his life in bits and pieces before he died. I've put his tale together as best I can, like assembling a jigsaw puzzle. The violent parts were told to me when I was older but have put them in order to avoid a choppy story. I have racked my brain to the point of insanity recalling memories of my beloved Gramps. I have also found that in the telling of his story, I must tell my own for the lives we have led are quite similar.

This story describes experiences seen through the eyes of a Japanese-American. Beginning in 1868 hundreds of thousands Japanese immigrated to Hawaii as contract labors for the thriving sugar and pineapple plantations. In Japan on the island of Suo Oshima, a sister city to the island of Kaua'i since 1963 in Yamaguchi Prefecture, there is a museum depicting Japanese immigration to Hawaii. His experiences brings a whole new perspective to all the writings about World War II and the Korean War. Gramps always hated that there were only a dozen or so books on the Korean War (1950-1953). None of these books mentioned Japanese Americans and how they were treated in the U.S. armed forces. There are fewer movies or television shows about the Korean War, apart from M.A.S.H. The Korean War, often called "The Forgotten War," overshadowed by a victory in the Second World War and again by America's eventual defeat in the Vietnam War.

The Second World War, on the other hand, is frequently covered and discussed. It was known as the glorious war; a war fought against ruthless dictators to free oppressed people. There are hundreds, if not thousands of books, articles, TV shows and movies about it. And yet despite all the coverage there are so many untold stories. For example, writings are rare about the impact of the war in Denmark and the Scandinavian countries.

Many or most in my family have not heard these personal accounts by my grandfather, and now it is available for the whole world. He believed that it's the duty of every generation to inform the next generation about what they have lived through. He would say with conviction, "Every generation must tell the next generation all about their struggles, their victories and failures. If the generations that succeed us are supposed to have a bright future, how the hell will they ever do that if the past isn't known to them?" When he told me his tales, my grandfather told me that remembering his personal experiences may not guarantee a brighter future, "but it will ensure the hope of it."

So, these are mine and my grandfather's stories, mostly unfiltered, somewhat uncensored and written by his youngest grandson, by me. If you feel as if you've been sucked into wonderous world, then I've done my job.

Some words may not make sense to you. Gramps sometimes spoke in the unique language called "Pidgin." The proper term is Hawaiian Creole English. It is a fractional language made up from the different languages of Native Hawaiians, Asian immigrants, and the Portuguese. Pidgin arose in the immigrant camps for the plantations. Workers were placed in camps and divided by ethnicity, so they would not learn how to talk to each other and find out each other's differing wages. However, the plan backfired and it gave birth to Hawaiian Pidgin, which my grandfather spoke at times.

I do hope you enjoy the stories that were the fabric of my childhood.

Much Mahalo (thanks) and Aloha,
Kyle

Every great story begins with either a love of something or a curiosity of something, this is ours..

Chapter 1

Beginnings

When asked who your idol or hero is, what comes to mind? Famous people, actors, sports players, and musicians to name a few. For me, the answer didn't lie with the names of the famous but was always the same: my Grandpa, Kinjiro Kabazawa. His nickname was Ken. He would truly become the most amazing person I had ever known. Grandpa Kabazawa was my Mom's dad. She, my Mom, was the third of four children and was a native of Kauai. My Dad, on the other hand, was the second of three boys and a native of the Big Island or the Island of Hawaii. Since my parents settled on Kauai and had a child, relatives needed to step in to help with watching me while they were at work. I got to spend lots time with my maternal Grandparents, which was a thrill to me. I was the youngest of their three grandkids. The other two, a boy and a girl from my aunty, my mom's older sister, had a large age gap of eleven and eight years from my age.

My Grandpa Kabazawa was a typical Japanese-American man, quiet and loved food. He was very warm, loving and knowledgeable in just about everything. He was a Nisei or second generation Japanese Americans who unlike their immigrant parents called Issei were born in the United States. With a question mark arch for a back he stood at a short four foot five. I would later learn in his prime he stood at five foot five. His eye color was brown but to me it looked more of a light shade of blue. He wore large gold framed glasses and was mostly blind in one eye. His hair a mixture of black and white was always kept neat and short. His mug was also always clean and well shaved. His shinny gums were all rosy pink. He didn't have teeth for most of my life due to various infections. His voice tender and warm, spoken with a light accent of Hawaii. His laugh, deep and contagious. The man, despite all the hardships he endured was still calm and cool.

My earliest memory is as follows: I was five years old and was playing explorer. I ran through their house and made my way to their bedroom. The closet was shared by Grandpa on the right and Grandma on the left. I slid the thick tan colored wooden door, opening up Grandpa's side. I ran my tiny fingers through his hanging clothes. I looked up and something caught my eye. High up on the top shelf sat this round, rustic Danish Butter cookie tin. It dangled a few inches off the edge. The iconic blue paint was chipping and the dark brown color of rust was very visible. It was too high up to grab and there wasn't anything inside the closet I could climb up on. I looked on Grandpa's side of the bed and found a stool. I grabbed it and positioned it directly in line with the aged tin. I struggled as I stood my tip toes and stretched myself to grab the tin. After a moment my fingernails caught the round rim of the tin's bottom. It moved a couple of inches off and was now almost halfway off the shelf. I determined to get that old tin down, tried once more, and managed to knock it off the shelf. The tin crashed loudly onto the hard wooden floor. The tin's contents spilled out all over the floor. Old black and white pictures, an old folded up map, and a dozen metal objects.

Grandpa arrived to his room in a half panic.

His back in the usual hunch like a question mark. He stood with his hunch at around four foot five.

"Damn it boy! Be careful!" Gramps said. He panted.

"Sorry Grandpa. What's this?" I asked. I picked up the largest shield like pin.

Gramps looked at me and he took the multi colored shield like pin from my hand. He looked over the large pin in the silence and then he looked at me.

"This is the Order of Victory. It's a military award. The base is platinum. Its edges and side are of diamonds. This red here that make up the five corners of the star is synthetic ruby. When this was made the ruby color had to all match. Now, with real stones-" Gramps stopped and looked at my face. He began to laugh.

Some years he reveal the reason he suddenly stopped abruptly. It was because he realized he was explaining gemstones to a five year old!

"Did you get it in the war?" I asked.

"Yeah, I did. In fact I got all of these here from the same war and the same guy," he said. He pointed to the other military medals scattered on the ground.

"In Korea?" I asked.

"No, I'll let you on a secret this was the war I fought before Korea," Gramps said. He winked at me.

"Wow, so you fought in two wars? I asked, wide eyed.

"Yes, I did," he said. He sat on the bed.

"Can you tell me about it?" I asked.

Gramps let out a heavy sigh and laid the award next to him on the bed. He stared at the wall behind me for a moment.

"Okay what do you want to know?" Gramps asked.

"Everything," I said, wide-eyed.

Grandpa was born on March 22, 1926, on the island of Kaua'i in what then was the Territory of Hawaii.

Grandpa was the fourth child of his parents. They lived in Waimea town on the west side of the island, which at the time was the epicenter of Kaua'i. His siblings and him were of the *Nisei* generation, or second-generation Japanese. Unlike their parents, they were born in the United States.

In Hawaii during the 1930s, sugar plantations were big business. One of Grandpa's first jobs as a youth was a waterboy, fetching water to thirsty plantation field workers in Waimea. His next job was tending cows at the Waimea Dairy. He later spent his entire career milking the cows and then delivering milk, which he did until he retired.

Life was simple on Kaua'i in the 1930s. Televisions, computers and video games did not exist. Life was mostly extremely hard physical labor. In his rare free time, he shoreline fished with bamboo hand poles, played harmonica, or just hung out with the guys from work. An avid fan of boxing, he listened to many fights on the family's little shortwave radio in the house. Their radio was one of the finer things the family owned.

For fun Gramps and friends stole watermelons from a local watermelon patch. He and a few local boys would head to the patch, crouch low, make bird sounds and Gramps would aim his BB gun at the sky and fire. They would then would make believe a bird had landed in the patch. They would run into the patch and cut off the watermelons and hastily run out of there.
Yes, he was a rascal for sure!

Like many of his generation Grandpa could read and write fluently the language of his parents. This dual knowledge would prove to be vital in ways he could never in his wildest dreams ever imagine.

Everything changed when Gramps was age 15. On Sunday morning, December 7, 1941. The Japanese military unleashed their air force and navy on U.S. Military installations at Pearl Harbor, Naval Air Station in Barbers Point, Wheeler Army Airfield, and Naval Air Station Kaneohe Bay, Oahu.
They knew nothing would ever be the same again.

Some days later on Kaua'i, his older brother Kentaro rushed into the house at break-neck speed. (Kentaro went by "Jack" and he called my Grandpa "Ken.")

Jack was out of breath. Ken, he said, his chest heaving, "armed soldiers are goin' door to door and ransacking Japanese houses."

"They destroying stuff, too?" He asked, shooting up from his chair.

"Yeah," Uncle Jack nodded.

Gramps frantically looked around their small living room. The most valuable things he saw were the framed family photos. "Let's stash the pictures."

The brothers grabbed as many pictures as they could find. They managed to remove some of the photos from their frames but regrettably not all of them. They hid them under their shirts and in their pockets.

Ten minutes later, the door burst open. Six armed U.S. Army soldiers stormed the house. At this moment, their parents came to the front door. Right in front of him, the soldiers cocked their rifles and pointed them at them. The entire family stood there huddled together. Gramps could see in the soldiers' eyes that they were scared, but they were more confident because they were armed. Jack grabbed grandpa's arm to hold him back from charging at the soldiers. Good thing. Gramps imagined that if he had charged at them, he would have been shot. They were so afraid that they would shoot at their own shadows.

In command the soldiers sternly asked, "Are there any weapons in the house?"

"If you lookin' for my .22 rifle," Jack spat. "you go dive in the sewer," His hand clenched into a fist at his side.

The commander sent two soldiers to search through the family's tiny house for anything related to Japan. The other four soldiers tensely watched the Japanese family. Their weapons stayed trained at their hearts. He could hear the dresser in a bedroom being ripped open and its contents dumped all over the floor. The soldiers then tore into the cabinet in front of them and threw everything out of it. With the butts of their rifles, they smashed all the remaining framed pictures of them family in Japan. Right before their eyes, they bashed in the *butsudan*, the Japanese home alter. These men came into the family house and just tore it all to hell!

Finally, one of the soldiers came out of the bedroom, "Hey, look at this," he said, holding in has hand the family's shortwave radio. He lifted it up as if he'd found a prize.

"Oh, we gotta take this!" the squad leader exclaimed. The other soldier put the family's radio in his pocket and started to leave.

As the soldiers went out the door Grandpa's father snapped out, *"Bakatari!"*

Jack looked shocked and let Gramps go.

One of the soldiers stuck his head back through the door. He looked straight at grandpa, his eyes wary, and said, "Hey, Jap what did your father just say?"

"Oh, he said you guys are good men," Grandpa responded with a smile.

The solider smiled back and left. As they headed back up the road, he could hear the soldiers calling each other *bakatari*. Despite the upset, he had to laugh out loud. The Japanese term doesn't mean "good men," It means stupid, moron, and idiot.

This incident was only the beginning of what would follow for the Japanese and Japanese Americans in Hawaii. Things were about to get a hell of a lot worse.

Immediately after the Pearl Harbor attack, the process began of rounding up all the people of Japanese ancestry. Military personnel and agents of the Federal Bureau of Investigation (FBI) at first only took any Japanese person who held a prominent position in the community. They took priests, teachers, lawyers, cops, territory guardsmen, and some businessmen as well as nearly everyone of Japanese ancestry who was involved in politics. On the mainland it was far worse, such as removing every Japanese and Nisei from the coasts. Regardless of our loyalty to the United States of America, they were treated like dangerous enemies.

In mid December 1941, a small force of U.S. Army soldiers rolled up to Waimea High School in a line of big army trucks. A ranking officer ordered the release of all the male students from class to help the army fortify the beaches to repel a Japanese invasion. They jumped onto the trucks, which brought them to the beach. The soldiers found some Filipinos and Chinese men and youth helping the soldiers set up machine guns.

To set themselves apart, many Chinese and Filipinos volunteered to help the *haole* (Caucasian) soldiers. However, the army didn't trust the Japanese near the weapons. They were told to string barbed wire all along the beach.

Gramps took off his shirt because it was so damn hot working under the Westside sun, and used it to wipe his face. At some point he dropped the shirt and kept working. When he went looking for it later, he found the shirt was laying right next to one of the machine guns. He tried to grab his shirt but was halted in his tracks.

"Hey, stop that Jap!" one of the soldiers yelled at the top of his lungs.

The solider who'd yelled at Gramps was draped with belts of machine gun bullets. The GI dove for the machine gun, pulled a string of ammunition from around his neck, slammed it into the gun, cocked it, and jammed the long steel barrel against the young Japanese American's forehead.

Other soldiers came running towards the scene. They also cocked their weapons and pointed them at Grandpa.

He tried to explain. "I just wanted…"

"Shut the hell up, you dirty Jap!" another soldier shouted.

A lieutenant walked up in back of him, cocked his .45 caliber Colt pistol and pressed it into the back of his head. He felt the pistol's cold steel as it pressed up against his head tightly. He flinched just slightly because of the coldness of the barrel. His heart pounded so hard in his chest he thought it was going to burst out. He never took his eyes off the guy who jammed the machine gun into his forehead.

"If you have the balls," Grandpa yelled feeling more angry than afraid, "then pull the damn trigger!"

Still watching him closely, the soldiers started giving one another sidelong glances, plainly seeking reassurance that they really heard what the young Japanese American teen just yelled in plain English. After a few more tense moments, which for him and all involved must have felt like an eternity, the soldiers started lowering their weapons.

"All right," the Lieutenant said. "I think that's enough work for the day. If any of you even breathe a word of this to anyone, I will have you detained. Understood?"

"Yes, sir!" they all replied in unison.

The soldiers herded all of the "Japs" back onto the trucks, and they went back to the school.

The next day government agents knocked on the family's front door and asked to speak with Gramps. They asked a few questions and left. Seems what he did on the beach reached the soldiers' superiors, and it would forever change everything for him.

The bombing of Pearl Harbor had set in motion a personal string of devastating consequences that no one could have ever foreseen. It would eventually come to a head with me. My fraternal side of the family was sent to the newly constructed Japanese American Relocation Camps. They were more commonly known as the Internment Camps. My paternal Great Grandfather was a Shinto minister. After the bombing at Pearl the U.S. Government took every Japanese national and Japanese American who held high positions or positions of influence like teachers, cops, businessmen, and minsters. How the story goes is that on the night of December 7, 1941 great gramps was forcibly removed from his house and detained at Kilauea Military Camp, Big Island. He was then sent to Sand Island, Oahu. Later he was transferred to somewhere in San Francisco where he was reunited with his family. The family, now whole again was sent to Jerome internment in Arkansas and later Gila River in Arizona.

Chapter 2

"Volunteered" And Attacked

A couple weeks after the beach incident, two Caucasian men came to the house. They were dressed in suits. They came from Washington DC.

"We are under direct orders from President Roosevelt," said Suit One.

"Apparently, your little incident on the beach a couple weeks ago turned his head," said Suit Two.

"So, what do you want with me?" Gramps asked, walking to the sink to fill up his cup with water.

"The President has taken a look into your family and found some interesting ties," said Suit One.

"Like what?" He scoffed. He took a sip of water.

Grandpa pulled out a chair from the kitchen table and sat down. The chair loudly scraped the floor. He pushed himself closer to the table. He did not offer a chair to the two men from Washington.

"Like your two great uncles in Japan," Suite One said. The first is a careerist soldier, and the other is a bodyguard at the Imperial Palace."

"So, what?" He felt belligerent.

"Well, now that you mentioned my uncles in Japan, how about their photos the GIs destroyed when they barged in and fucked up the house, huh? Government soldiers destroyed my house with no warrant. Tell me, please, why I would want to work for the president! Tell me now!" Grandpa slapped his hand on the table. Everything on it rattled.

"We understand your frustration and anger," said Suit Two, walking over and leaning on the table. His face looks compassionate and warm. "But this is not about you. Those soldiers had the wrong idea that every Japanese person in America was responsible for lighting up Oahu. The president wants to counter that image of your people, who are much more visible that the Germans and the Italians. This is why we are here."

Suit Two's speech sounded like a sales pitch. He never broke eye contact. Gramps could tell that he believed every word he spoke. Hell, he clung onto every word the suit spoke. Gramps was no fool, but the suit was so convincing, and he was so fed up with how he was treated by the soldiers that he ate it all up.

"Okay so what is it that you want with me?" Gramps leaned back in his chair.

"The President has chosen you as the perfect candidate," said Suit Two. "Candidate for what?" He asked.

The two men quickly glanced at each other and then back at Gramps.

"Mr. Roosevelt wants you to be his man on the inside, "said Suit One. "Inside of what? Wait, you are saying you want me to be a *spy*?" He was shocked.

"Yes, we want you to spy for your country, said Suit Two. He pulled out a chair and sat down at the table." Provided that you still consider this your country."

"Yes, I do," Grandpa leaned forward, now interested "if I agree, where? When?"

"Philippines. You leave in one month," said Suit One. He pulled out a handkerchief and wiped the sweat off his face.

"And if I refuse?" He asked.

"Well, you saw what happened to your kind after Pearl," Suit One said. Gramps nodded.

"Your entire family, including you, will be detained until the war is over," Suit Two declared.

"Well, in that case, when do we being?" In that moment, without having much of a choice about it, even though Gramps was only 15 years old, he agreed to be a spy for Roosevelt.

"Wait so you were like Alex Rider?" I asked, intrigued.

"Yeah I guess I was," Gramps said with a short laugh.

In the aftermath of all the raids on Japanese families on Kaua'i, many of the families that weren't taken, switched religion from Buddhism to either

Christianity or often Catholicism. They did so to avoid feeling more of the repercussions from the bombing of Pearl Harbor. On Grandpa's street, all the Japanese families converted except theirs and one other. One Christian group gained followers by saying the world was going to end in seven days. They met in plain sight. Many newly converted Japanese families followed them and gave what little money they had for donations. The group was spearheaded by *haoles*. With each day they counted down, their following grew.

Grandpa watched them from afar as they met day after day. On the morning of the seventh day, the people went out and found the *haoles'* little camp was gone. There was not a single trace of the camp, none whatsoever. He laughed up at that one boy! Those *haoles* were right about one thing. The world did end for all of their followers. After Gramps had his laugh, he became filled with rage on the fact that these haoles preyed on the Japanese when they were at their most vulnerable.

One day he answered a knock on the front door. There was a middle-aged *haole* lady. She was dressed in a white dress and cradled a black bible under her arm.

"Are your parents around?" She looked around the inside of the house from the open door.

"Whatever you want to say to them you can say to me," Gramps stated.

"Well, I heard that your family was one of the only holdouts on converting to Christ," she stated. She preached at him for a few minutes about Jesus and how everyone had embraced Him already.

Grandpa interrupted her sales pitch. "Doesn't it say somewhere in the book, 'Thou shalt not kill or lie."

"Yes, it does," she seemed taken back.

"Then why the hell do you people spread lies and prey on us, huh? Why do you come up on our property and try to jam your scripture your bullshit stories to change us! Tell me that!"

She stammered out an objection, but he was on a roll.

"As loyal Americans, it's our given right to believe in what we want to believe. We all believe in one God. We just call him by a different name, and we have different beliefs to go along with it," Gramps shouting at her, filled with rage. "Now get the hell off of my property- *now!*"

His mother came by the door to see what the ruckus was about. She looked at the woman, then at Gramps and demanded, "What's goin' on here?"

"Oh I'm so sorry, Ma'am," said the preacher lady, "but your son here is goin' straight to hell." She pointed her index finger to him.

"Oh yeah?" he yelled. "Well, I'll see you there, bitch. Now get the hell outta here!"

That lady spun around and left the yard so fast that she should have run track. After that, no one came to bother them about converting.

"Huh so that's why the Christian guys don't come here?" I asked.

Grandpa nodded.

In the early hours of 30th December, Nawiliwili Harbor on Kaua'i was hit with at least 15 three-inch shells from a Japanese submarine about four miles off shore. Gramps wasn't personally there to see it, but it was big news the rest of the day. Nawiliwili Harbor is on the southeastern side of the island, just outside the town of Lihue. The war had come to Kaua'i. Most of the rounds didn't go off, so there wasn't too much damage and no one was killed. A round did blast shrapnel through an entire house. Another round started a small sugar cane fire. One round punctured a Shell Oil gas storage truck, which didn't explode. From what Grandpa heard later that day, as rounds harmlessly hit the water, they made big splashes and shot water some ten feet up in the air. Sometime later that day somebody ran over a round with a truck but thankfully it didn't go off. This was the one and only attack that Kaua'i sustained during the entire Second World War.

In the aftermath of the Kaua'i attack, Grandpa's training began on 2nd January, 1942. He was flown to Schofield Barracks on Oahu for special training. When he arrived at Schofield, there was a small section roped off just for him to train.

Suit one and two stayed with him through the entire special training course, which lasted three weeks. The instructor, he later found out, came from some Army Base on the mainland. Gramps learned the basics of using various firearms like shooting a Colt .45 pistol with only one hand. He mastered how to fire and field strip the M1 Garand rifle and Thompson submachine gun. He learned how to throw the MK II Pineapple Fragmentation Grenade. He was trained in knife fighting, bayonet attacks and advanced hand- to- hand combat. He had taken Judo for a few years, so the hand-to-hand was relatively easy. He did a lot of PT, physical training, which consisted of runs, jumping jacks, push-ups, and sit ups.

The most fun part of the training was the two days Grandpa did parachute training. He did a total of six jumps, three at night and three during the day. In the training, he mastered how to pack his own chute. he learned to pull the ripcord as soon as he went out the door of the airplane. As the plane got closer to the drop zone, one of the crew would yelled "Stand up and hook on." Hooking on means to clip the ripcord onto what's called a static line. The wind whips through the airplane. The first man out got to see a great view. There was a large and clearly visible light inside the airplane. That light stayed red, but when it turned green, it's *cowabunga* time!

"Wait so you did the same training as the real guys from *Band Of Brothers* the show?" I interrupted.

"Yeah, I did. And you know what that army cadre was kinda like Dick Winters," Gramps laughed.

They next trained him in the art of "tradecraft"—things like dead drops and sleight-of-hand techniques. He memorized the uniform collar ranks and insignias of the Imperial Japanese Army or IJA. The instructor would show him pictures of the collar ranks on flash card pictures, and he would shout out the rank in both English and Japanese. They tested his Japanese skills, both speaking and writing. He would have to write in Kanji and then translate it to English.

As training went on, he got to know more about the agents and his instructor. The Army instructor was a lifer named Marvin from Pittsburgh, Pennsylvania. In the 1920s after Marvin graduated from University of Pittsburgh, he decided to travel around Asia. He went all over Asia but took a particular interest in Japan. He spent five months and became fluent in both speaking and writing in Japanese. Upon returning to the States he joined the U.S. Army. President Roosevelt personally sent him down to train him, and as he later found out this was the last thing Marvin did in the service. He retired and spent the rest of his days soaking up the sunshine in a large house on a pink beach of the Bahamas.

The two suits were Daniel and Tom. They and Gramps became quite good friends. Daniel was from Saint Paul, Minnesota, and he was 30 years old. Tom was from Arlington, Virginia and he was 28 years old. They had faith in him and said that he would be successful in his mission. Gramps was not so confident. For one, he had too much anger. For another thing, he was too eager to prove himself.

Grandpa was told that the Army had an intelligence agency, the Counter Intelligence Corps (CIC). Prior to the bombing of Pearl Harbor it was called Corps of Intelligence Police (CIP). There was a guy from Hawaii by the name of Albert Kadena, who was in it. He was in the Philippines when the Japanese attacked there, and he was arrested. After his released, since he was exposed as a spy, his spying days ended. Kadena became part of the newly formed Military Intelligence Service (MIS), a part of the U.S. military made up of mostly Japanese-Americans whose job was to translate captured enemy documents and conduct interrogations. Some of them were attached to units searching for Imperial troops in the jungles of the Pacific. The MIS men mainly stayed behind the lines at headquarters. Gramps was not one of these MIS men in the Philippines. He would operate far behind enemy lines, with almost no one knowing him and his real mission. He was certain if caught by the Allies, the MIS boys would never believe him. In that situation he could only hope it would be by Kauai boys.

Just before his training was over Marvin told Gramps some very good cautionary advice.

"Remember Ally don't mean friend. No matter how charming and attractive they will be. The only things you can fully trust is your training, your faith and yourself. Got it? Good. Now give those bastards hell!" Marvin said.

Gramps loosely follow this and it would later prove more than once as the key that saved his life.

After training was over, he was given a one-week break before he was sent overseas. He went back home to Kaua'i. He told his parents what he could about his country "asking" him to fight for her. He never forgot his father's response in Japanese. He gave Gramps a big hug and said in Japanese, "Good. Remember never dishonor our name."

His mother, on the other hand was scared and nervous for Gramps. He was heading into a war at age 15. She knew the alternative if he did not go, so she couldn't really object. The main problem was that as a spy, unlike regular GI, he could not have any contact with them. No mail. Nothing. Was he afraid? Yes most definitely, yes!

Almost immediately after the bombing of Pearl, blackouts and strict curfews were installed on all of the Hawaiian Islands. This was called martial law. The blackouts brought a new job, a light marshal or light warden. The job was given to an armed GI or armed member of the Kauai Volunteers (KV) to patrol neighborhoods to ensure no light could be seen from outside a house. If even just one ray of light peaked through, loud bangs on the door would be heard followed by a scolding and an order to cut that light. The reasons for the blackouts came from war hysteria. The U.S. government believed that the light from houses could signal Japanese naval and air forces on the waters off the islands and the coast of the mainland. The other reason was that light from houses and building would make easily seen targets for bombings. Another thing that they believed that farmers of Japanese ancestry could rearrange their crops to send messages to Japanese plans in the skies. It's pretty ridiculous thing to think about now. Most nights, Gramps would go outside and look up at all the stars that lit up the sky. While on leave back on Kaua'i, he was terrified that this would be the last week that he would get to see the Hawaiian sky.

Grandpa knew that he was trained well, but if the Japanese found out that he was spying for the Americans he would be tortured and executed. He had heard how gruesome the Japanese torture could be. He had no idea how long he could hold out if he was captured.

During this week, he went to the beach and up to the mountains of Koke'e on the west side of Kaua'i. he figured it would be a long time before he would be back, so he wanted to enjoy it. He savored the smell of the salt air at the beach. He grabbed a handful of sand and felt every grain fall out of his hand and back to the beach. When he was up in Koke'e, he savored the taste of wild berries on a trail in the mountains. He brushed his hand against the trees. He felt the sharpness of the bark, the smoothness of the leaves. He closed his eyes and let the sunlight with its warmth soak into his body. He made himself feel calm and at peace, for if it would be the last time he would ever be here at home on Kaua'i, he wanted to bask in these moments and memories. He had a feeling that he might need them later on.

I hiked with Gramps up in Kokee only once, in April 2006. Gramps was 80 and I was 11! We just dropped Grandma off at an appointment at the Waimea Hospital and we drove the mountains. We drove with the windows down and I felt the temp drop.

"Grandpa? Are we going all the way to the top?" I asked. Endless rows of lush green gigantic trees zoomed pass my window.

"Yeah, I think it will be a nice change of scenery for bout of us," he said.

"Is Grandma dying?" I asked, I looked at him.

"No!" Gramps said, his eyes still on the road.

"Are *you* dying?" I asked, I still looked at him.

"No, one is dying! I just wanted to spend time with you outside our houses," he said. He looked at me.

"Oh okay," I said. I went back to look out my open window.

We went to the Kalalau lookout and parked at the last parking stall there. The place was as usual packed with tourists coming and going. We walked up the steps and up to the lookout itself. It was a beautiful cloudless mid-morning day. All the birds sang their tunes. The flowers all in full bloom, a multicolor paradise. We walked down the trail and all the way tourists from all over globe stopped us for a picture. Gramps told them he was doing this as a belated birthday present for he and I. He took a picture for Honeymooners from Paris. They chatted in fluent French and the couple seemed to be so impressed with him, that they asked me to take a second picture with Gramps in it! They waved as we continued our trek down. The next bunch we passed was an Italian Bachelorette group. They too asked for Gramps to take their picture and he spoke Italian flawlessly! They were so impressed with him and I that they asked another passerby to take a picture with all of us. Oh, how I wished that moment lasted longer because those women, whose ages ranged from early 20s to early 30 were just absolutely beautiful and fit! They parted with us and we continued our descent down.

Between taking pictures and impressing tourists Gramps pointed out to me all the plants and animals up there. We also spoke about the past and life.

"Grandpa? What's the real reason we're up here hiking?" I asked. I stopped waking and looked at him.

"Well, I guess there's no foolin' you huh boy?" He said. He stopped and looked right in my eyes.

He let lout a long sight and began to speak.

"I won't be around forever but these places will be. I came up here many times thought my life. I came up here before I shipped off to both wars. But, mostly I come up here cause I find peace. I let all the shit I carry loose up here. In turn I let every ray of sunlight or moonlight, tree, plant, flower, waterfall, and animal in. Here I find peace. At Shingon they teach inner peace with the chanting of sutras but here is where I have always found it. I'm showing you these places so you can find it too up here. My father did the same with me when I was your age and you'll do the same with your kids," Gramps opened up. He put his hand on my shoulder.

"Wow. Thank you Grandpa," I said. I tapped his hand on my shoulder.

"You're welcome boy. And besides there is a hell of a view!" Gramps said. He flash a wide smile.

"Oh, yeah more than one!" I quipped up with a giant smile.

We both laughed up a storm.

After we finished laughing we continued our trek. We made it half way before Grandpa's legs began to give out. We stopped and rested for a bit before we made the trek back. After we made it out we jumped back into the car and drove back to the hospital to pick up Grandma. Until this writing I have never shared this story. As I mentioned in the intro I wrote, nearly all of these stories have never been told until now.

After Grandpa's death five years later I planned to take a swan dive off from the same lookout point we took numerous pictures for tourists. In the end I decided against it but not for the reasons you think. One reason was that the place is always packed with tourist and I didn't want to ruin their vacation and scar them for life by my death. The second reason was that I didn't get my driver's license until I was 19!

Gramps had no idea how long of a journey he was about to embark. Nor did he have any idea as to where his service would take him and whom he would meet along his unforeseen adventure into a world entrenched in war.

Once the week was over in February, Grandpa was put on a plane and flown to Oahu. Tom told him that before he was sent into the Philippines, President Roosevelt wanted to talk with him face- to-face in Washington DC. He met with Daniel and Tom in Oahu, and they flew to California. They flew in a Douglas C-47 Skytrain, the military version of the Douglas DC -3. The C-47 "gooney bird" later in the war was used as a troop and supply transport.

When Gramps first hopped in, he was amazed by how much room it had. There were only four of them, including the pilot, a countryman named Jimmy, so it was quite cozy. Prior to leaving Kaua'i, he was told to bring warm clothes, which he did. They landed at a military base called March Field (now called March Air Reserve Base) in Southern California or SoCal to refuel and eat. Back on the airplane, they ate snacks composed of chips, candy and soft drinks as they continued to fly east. The next refueling stop was Glenview Naval Air station in Glenview, Illinois. Grandpa had never seen snow in person. This was a highlight of the trip along with the bare trees and squirrels.

"Ken, stay with the plane while we get breakfast," Daniel instructed. He took out his sidearm, a Colt M1911 .45 semiautomatic pistol from his jacket, chambered a round and stuck it back in his jacket.

"Okay, got it," Grandpa replied. He took in his new surroundings.

"What do ya want us to bring back for you?" Tom asked. He pulled out his wallet to inspect it.

"A stack of waffles, syrup, and easy-over eggs with some strips of bacon," Grandpa answered still gazing around.

"Anything else? Tom flipped through the bills in his wallet.

"Uh, a bunch of Hershey bars and soda," Gramps replied.

Gramps caught sight of a small furry creature, darting from one tree branch to another, but didn't tell the guys about it.

"Okay what flavors of soda?" Daniel pulled out a tissue and blew his nose hard.

"Coke, Dr. Pepper and Sarsaparilla," Gramps said with a smile.

"You got it, kid." Tom finished counting his money and put his wallet away. "And remember stay out of sight. This isn't like back home, if they see you they will kill you."

"They can try," Gramps quipped, cracking a half grin.

The men nodded and walked off to forage for food. After they were out of sight, Gramps laid on his back in the snow. His teeth clicked nonstop. Even with a thick jacket with a fur lining and gloves, he was cold. He could see his own breath, and he laughed at the sight of it. He blew out so much air that the sky seemed to be spinning! Good thing he was already lying down. He stopped hyperventilating. Once he could see straight, again he moved his feet and arms side-to-side and made snow angels. When he finished, he just laughed and laid there on the snow, chilly but content, until the men came back an hour later.

"What are you doing?" Tom asked, looking at Gramps lie in the snow.

"Makin' snow angels," Gramps replied with a big goofy smile that showed all his teeth.

Jimmy laughed.

"You know, back home, I used to do that all the time," Jimmy said. He bent down and looked at Gramps.

"Where was that again?" Gramps asked as he turned his head to the side.

"Oh, Milford, Nebraska," Jimmy rubbed his gloved hands together for warmth.

"Let's eat," Tom said.

Daniel walked over and extended his hand. Grandpa grabbed him and he helped him to sit up in snow. Tom and Daniel sat down next to him in the snowy ground, and they began to eat. Jimmy, their pilot, put all but four drinks in their cooler on the plane and sat down, with them to eat. They cracked jokes and had a riot of a time as they ate. After they finished eating they jumped back in the plane and continued to Washington DC.

When they landed at some airfield in DC, a car waited there to take Tom, Daniel, Jimmy, and Gramps to the White House. Once they got to the White House, Daniel and Tom led the way to the Oval Office. Before they opened the door they stopped and turned to Gramps.

Tom said, "The President has requested this talk to be with him and you only."

"Where will you all be?" Gramps asked.

"Waiting out here, Ken," Daniel said. He smiled briefly.

Tom opened the door, and Gramps walked into the Oval office. He closed it behind Grandpa.

An old man sat behind a desk in the room. He was looking over papers when Gramps came in. His famous cigarette holder rested in an ashtray.

"Kinjiro, welcome to Washington," he said. He wheeled himself out from behind the desk to greet him. In a wheelchair, Franklin Delano Roosevelt, President of the United States of America, held out his hand to him.

"Thank you, sir," Gramps said. They shook hands.

"Please, call me Franklin, and take a seat."

"Okay, thank you, Franklin."

FDR smiled kindly at Gramps and motioned him into a chair in front of the desk. He retook his place behind the desk.

"Drink?" he asked. He held up a bottle and two glasses.

"Yes, please," Gramps replied. He cracked his neck.

"You know you shouldn't be drinking at 15," Franklin said.

"Well, I shouldn't be heading off to war either," Gramps grinned.

"Touché," the president chuckled. He poured the amber liquor into the glasses and slid a glass across to him. Gramps picked up the glass, and looked at it. He didn't drink much.

"To winning the war," he said, holding up his glass in a toast.

Gramps stretched across his desk to clink glasses. "To winning the war." After one sip, they set their glasses on the desk and got right down to business.

"You know where you're being sent?" Franklin asked. He lifted his glasses and rubbed the bridge of his nose.

"The Philippines," Gramps leaned back in his chair.

"What do you know of Japan's progress there?"

"You mean the fact that the United States is getting nailed?"

"Yes." He sighed deeply. "Ken, I'm not gonna lie to you. It's hell out there, and it's only going to get worse." he paused to look directly at Gramps. He seemed to be shifting gears. His face grew more serious. "I'm sure you are well aware of the hatred against the Japanese in this country right now."

"Yes, I am," Gramps answered.

"The American public is screaming for revenge," he said, his voice grim. "I'm afraid that if I don't deliver what they want, they will find someone who will."

"So, what do you want me to do?" Grandpa leaned in closer.

"I am well aware that very few of the Japanese in this country are to blame for the attack on Oahu, but almost no one else shares this opinion. There are only four others who share this view, and I'm sure that you know three of them well," he said.

Gramps nodded. He meant his three traveling companions.

"Well, the military boys and intel boys fear that if we send Japanese-American troops in large numbers into the Pacific, in their eyes, as non-Asians, it will be hard to tell the difference between our troops and enemy soldiers. They fear our Japanese-American troops will not shoot an enemy solider if they recognize him as a family member or friend fighting on the other side. Another fear is that Imperial soldiers may switch uniforms, walk right into a U.S. camp and open fire." He tapped his finger on his desk. "Given all this, I'm afraid I must ask of more of you than I ever should." He looked square into Grandpa's eyes." I want you to infiltrate the ranks of the Imperials."

"What?" Gramps was shocked. Did he hear that right?

"I picked you because of your language skills and your family's standing with the Empire of Japan, but most of all, I chose you because you have courage, as noted from the incident on the beach."

Gramps took a big gulp from his glass, nearly choked, recovered, and said casually as he could, "So, what's the plan?" Inside he could barely believe what was happening.

From a drawer he pulled out a map of the Philippines, spread it out on the table and touched a dot on the map. "The plan is that you will parachute into Bataan in the Philippines. You will be wearing a U.S. Army uniform and armed with U.S. weapons. You will then surrender to the first Japanese patrol you find. You are to tell them your real name, tell them about your family, and say that you are a translator for U.S. troops. Say that you are tired of all the hostility from your fellow soldiers since the bombing of Pearl Harbor. Say that you are fed up with America and want to fight for the Imperial Army."

Gramps could imagine this plan working, if he was careful, and if he could lie well enough. He studied the map and tapped his finger on it. "After I land, do I have a contact?"

"Filipino guerrilla fighters are hiding all over the jungles there, but you want to work only with one man, named Virgilio. He's your contact. He will be at your landing site and will fill you in. Once you are accepted and trusted in the Imperial Army, your second objective is to feed Virgilio intelligence on troop movements, supply chains, the status of POWs, the state of morale in the camp, and anything else worth reporting. When you meet him, he will ask for a code, which is Pegasus." Roosevelt took an easy sip from his glass. "You are now a presidential agent, and your codename from now on is Dragon 577."

Gramps slowly pulled his gaze from the map and looked back into FDR's eyes, "What do I do if I'm discovered?" Gramps asked.

He really meant, what is the plan if he his cover is blown and or he is killed?

FDR took a breath and said, "Should you die out there your family will receive $100,000 not the usual $10,000 death benefits. In the event that you are compromised, if you can, you are to kill any and all Japanese soldiers in the camp and free any POWs held there. After that, meet up with Virgilio, and he will relay back to me that you have been compromised. "After that, stay hidden and await instructions." Roosevelt held his gaze.

Now Gramps had the big picture. He leaned back into his chair and relaxed. He was scared, sure, but somehow he knew he could do this. "Does the mission have a codename?"

"Officially, the mission doesn't exist, much like you. However, we're calling it Operation Trojan and its part of Project Annihilation. Annihilation's sole purpose is to win this war by any means necessary. As part of Annihilation, there is only a select group of people who knows of Operation Trojan and about you. Even the Vice President doesn't know about any of this. You are authorized to take any means necessary to maintain your cover. Should you have to shoot or torture any Americans and Allied personal to keep your cover, you do it. No questions asked." He placed his elbows on the table, interlaced his fingers.

"How often do I meet with Virgilio?"

"You meet with him every few days to ensure that you are not compromised. You two can figure out where in the jungle you want to meet. There will be other instructions that he will go over with you when you get there. If the Philippines does fall, and I fear it will fall, you will be my eyes and ears on the inside. You are what we call 'a vital independent variable of war.' We have a shorter new term that we came up with here, it's called 'born secret.' Meaning classified as top secret upon creation. That is what you are. You are not just a soldier, not just a spy. You are more than that." Franklin said.

"So, you don't think General MacArthur can hold against the Imperials?"

The president shook his head. "No, not at this time."

"I see, and does he know about me?"

"Yes, he has a need to know. He wanted me to place you under him, in fact, but I flat out refused. I need you to report only to me." The president emptied his glass.

"When does my mission start?"

"Effective immediately."

"Okay, in that case, who's flying me to the Philippines?"

"Jimmy will fly you. And if I'm not mistaken, uniforms, a parachute and weapons are onboard by now. I have the utmost confidence that you will succeed."

Gramps drained his glass dry, gulped hard to keep it down, and then set it back on the desk.

"Is there anything else before I walk into the fire?" Grandpa's belly burned from the drink.

"No, except I trust you to keep our little secret," he winked.

Gramps chuckled.

"Godspeed, Ken." President Roosevelt held out his hand.

They shook hands. "Thank you Franklin," Gramps stood to leave.

"Oh, one more thing," the president said. "You are completely off the books. Any and every shred of you and your activities will be destroyed at the end of this war. Your role will be forgotten. If you survive, and I believe you will, you are not to speak of anything you did or were involved in for a period of no less than 50 years."

Gramps nodded in agreement, and walked to the door. Gramps looked back at this great man with awe at the burden he must be carrying, and he closed the door softly behind him.

Just outside sat Grandpa's three buddies, waiting for him.

"So, when do ya leave?" Daniel asked.

"As soon as possible. And Jimmy, you're flying."

Jimmy nodded. He already knew.

"You know," said Tom," if I ever have a son I hope he's just like you."

"I second that," Daniel said. They hugged.

"Thank you, both of you," Gramps said. "I will never forget you."

"You better not forget us," Tom said with a half grin.

They all started to laugh.

"See you when I see you," Gramps said, and they all waved goodbye.

Gramps left the White House with Jimmy.

That was the last time Gramps ever saw Tom and Daniel. Some thirty years later he found out that they both served as paratroopers in the Normandy D-Day invasion on June 6, 1944. They both became highly decorated soldiers and served in Europe until the war was over in 1945. They went back home, got married and eventually settled down in Orlando, Florida. They each had four kids and remained friends as well as neighbors for the rest of their lives. Tom died in 1998, and Daniel died in 2001.

The car took Jimmy and Gramps back to the airfield. He stared out the window. Bare trees and snow raced past them.

"Beautiful, isn't it?" Gramps said still marveling at the winter surroundings.

"For a week, yeah," Jimmy said. "Any more than that, and it's fuckin' horrible!"

Gramps laughed.

They arrived at the airfield, boarded the airplane and flew off to Bataan.

Chapter 3

Into The Dragon's Mouth

Flying over the Philippines, the pair began to take heavy ground fire.
Ping! Pang! Ping! Bullets ricocheted off the airplane continuously for hours.
The one thing that Roosevelt neglected to mention to Gramps was that when
he would reach, Bataan he was going to be dropped right into an active
battle under heavy enemy fire. The Battle of Bataan raged from January 7th,
1942 and would end with the Japanese as victor on April 9th, 1942.
"You better put on the uniform!" Jimmy yelled over the engine room.
"Yeah!" Gramps yelled back.
Gramps unzipped a second duffle bag and there it was a U.S. Army
uniform. He pulled it out to examine it and noticed the three stripes on the
sleeve.
"Wow, a Sergeant," Gramps said in awe as his fingers glided over the
smooth stripes.
Grandpa hastily put on the uniform, pants and shoes. He walked across
the plane and grabbed a Thompson M1928 submachinegun and a Colt
M1911 .45 pistol with holster. He put the holstered sidearm on his hip and
slung the Tommy over his shoulder with the strap. He also took a bunch of
the fifty round drum magazines for the weapons and placed them in the

ammunition pouches on him. He also pulled out the parachute and placed it on his seat and walked over to Jimmy.

"How long more?" He asked.

"Uh about 25 minutes," Jimmy replied as bullets hit the outside of the airplane.

"Got it," Gramps replied and looked from the cockpit.

"Nice Sarge, huh?" Jimmy said. He glanced at Grandpa and noticed the stripes on his sleeve.

"Yeah, it's uh a nice surprise," Gramps replied. He looked at his sleeve. Jimmy nodded.

All of a sudden there was a loud explosion that shook the entire plane and they started to bank left towards the ground.

"OH FUCK!" Jimmy yelled with his eyebrows up and eyes wide.

"The hell was that?" Gramps shouted, startled.

"They hit the engine and we're goin' down!" He shouted back.

As Grandpa looked out the window all he could see was a massive amount of smoke coming from the side of the airplane.

"You got guns and a parachute?" Gramps yelled.

"Yeah!" He yelled back.

"How long can she fly?" Gramps yelled.

"10 minutes at most!" He responded.

"FUCK!" Gramps yelled.

Grandpa's heart pounded so hard that he thought it was gonna suddenly burst out of his chest. His lips were dry and his throat came so tight he couldn't swallow; he was freaking out and bad. As the severely damaged plane went out of control it twisted and turned everything around like clothes inside a washing machine. He closed his eyes; shut all the sounds around him and just concentrated on finding peace. As he found it his heart rate slowed and he could swallow again. He opened up his eyes and all the sound flooded back. Suddenly his training kicked into gear as if it was automatic. Despite finding mental peace, massive amounts adrenaline surged through his body and it didn't wear off for days.

As Jimmy managed to level out the airplane he steadily climbed back up to around 3,000 feet. Seven minutes after they got hit Jimmy and Gramps grabbed their gear and popped open the door. They also stuffed some hand grenades in their pocket and tossed a couple live ones in the airplane before they jumped out. The airplane exploded above them as they were in a free fall in midair. At a thousand feet they pulled their chutes open and it deployed perfectly. The pair landed on the jungle floor below and immediately took off their parachutes. With their Tommy guns at the ready they scanned the area for troop movement before they did anything else.

"All clear." Gramps said.

The pair swung their guns back over their shoulders and Gramps unfolded a map from his pocket.

"Okay so where the hell are we?" Gramps asked.

"We are here," Jimmy said. He pointed out a spot on the map.

"And the drop zone was supposed to be here," Gramps said. He pointed out on the map.

As Gramps eyeballed the distance by using the legend on the map he managed to figure out that they weren't that far off target.

"Okay we are 11 miles South of the DZ (drop zone). We gotta go North, this way," Gramps said. He pointed in the distance.

"You got a compass?" Grandpa asked.

"Yeah," Jimmy replied and pulled it out.

"Okay you be the navigator. I'll take point. You cover the rear," Gramps said. He gave him the map.

"Got it," he said. He took the map and placed it in a pocket on the inside of his uniform.

Gramps figured that if he was killed or captured when the Imperials would search him they would find nothing of intelligence value.

So, began the long walk to the DZ and it was not without surprises. About three miles into the walk Gramps heard voices and coming up from up ahead.

"Stop. Quickly follow me," Gramps whispered.

They got off the path and hid in behind trees and blended in with the dense jungle.

"Enemy patrol?" Jimmy whispered.

Gramps nodded.

The steps came closer and closer Grandpa's pulse raced and his fingers held his Tommy tightly. As the voices became clearer he managed to identify five separate voices all whom were speaking Japanese.

"Wait until they are right in front," Gramps whispered.

Jimmy nodded.

As Gramps stood behind the tree with the tommy in his hands he shut his eyes once again. He tuned out all sounds but the loud pounding of his heart. He breathed in and out slowly to slow down his racing heart until it was as steady as his breathing. Then, he opened his eyes and let the whole world come back to him. He was remembering a lesson of his training. The lesson was that they could train and advise him all they wanted but in the end the action is all up to him. That lesson he believed is true in combat and true in life. The Imperials were just about in front of them and he turned to Jimmy and nodded. Just like that they snapped into action. The pair jumped out from behind the trees and let their Tommy guns roar with rapid precision. To Gramps it seemed that everything went in slow motion like he could see every round as it hit the soldier and the blood spewed out from his body. Every shot was a hit and what seemed like minutes was over in seconds. Hell, he could even see the individual shell casings eject and fall onto the jungle floor. The Japanese Soldiers were all dead before they could fire a single shot. Hell, they were dead even before their bodies hit the ground.

The pair of them panted as they took cover back behind the trees. They ejected their empty magazines, loaded a full one and cocked it. They sprang back out to look for movement on the ground but saw not a single thing was moving. The men walked over to the bodies and dragged them to another position behind the trees. They searched all five bodies and found nothing useful. So, they hid the bodies with leaves and stripped them of their weapons. Jimmy took a Type 99 light machine gun and a Nambu pistol and Gramps took a Nambu pistol as well. They put the rest of the Japanese weapons in a separate pile and hid them with leaves as well. After that was over the pair continued on their long walk.

While they walked Gramps noticed that Jimmy's hand trembled and had ever since the ambush. So, he decided to try and chat with him in the hopes of calming him down.

"First time you ever kill anyone?" Gramps asked. He panted.

"Yeah," Jimmy replied. He panted.

"The first time's always the hardest. And you didn't freeze up so that's good." Gramps said. he wiped the sweat off his forehead with his sleeve.

Jimmy laughed.

"Yeah I guess so. How you holdin' up?" Jimmy asked. He knew it was Grandpa's first time whacking out someone too.

"Nerves are fried but besides that I'm good," Gramps conveniently lied. Gramps was in fact trying his best to conceal that fact that he was quite shaken up from the attack. He hadn't learned how to deal with the killing yet. However, he would come to terms with it soon but for now he was a concealed wreck. Four more miles later the pair again heard voices but this time they chose to stand and fight straight. They waited on the trail out in the open to get visuals before opening up. As the lead man became visible it was clear that he was not an Imperial Soldier but an armed Filipino. He was leading a group of 10 all of whom were armed. As the men spotted each other they all had their weapons chambered and ready.

"Pegasus." Gramps said with his weapon trained on the man's head.

"You are Dragon 577?" He asked in a thick Filipino accent. He stared down the business end of Grandpa's tommy.

Gramps nodded. He lowered his Tommy and gave a thumbs up to Jimmy to lower his as well.

"I am Virgilio," he pointed to himself.

"This is my pilot –

"Tell him I'm Merlin," Jimmy said. He interrupted Gramps, took out a stick of gum and popped one in his mouth.

"This is Merlin," Gramps said in Filipino to Virgilio.

"Merlin?" Gramps asked. He turned to Jimmy on his right side.

"President Roosevelt gave me that code to use in case I ever got shot down here," Jimmy said. He loudly chewed his gum.

"Friends!" Virgilio yelled with a smile.

After that everyone in his group including himself lowered their weapons.

"Come I take you to our camp" Virgilio said in Filipino.

"You guys are far from camp, no?" Grandpa asked in Filipino.

"No, we had to relocate yesterday because of Japanese attack," he replied in Filipino and he glared at Gramps with his eyes.

Birds twittered and sung their sweets sounds as they flew above them.

"What's he sayin'?" Jimmy asked with an anxious expression on his face.

Jimmy walked closer to Gramps to hear and swung his tommy over his shoulder.

"They are takin' us to their new camp cause the old one got hit yesterday," Gramps replied.

Gramps wiped the sweat from his forehead.

"In the attack we lost half of our force including three U.S. soldiers," Virgilio said in Filipino with an undertone of anger in his voice.

"The last attack they lost half of their guys including three of our soldiers," Gramps translated to Jimmy.

"Damnit!" Jimmy exclaimed wide eyed.

The group walked for about a half hour until they got to the Filipino guerrilla camp. Grandpa cradled his tommy at the ready. The camp had six small two man tents and two larger tents. The tents were all made of wood and leaves from the jungle. There was a small fire pit in the center of the camp for warmth and cooking.

"The small tents are living quarters and the larger ones are supplies, pantry and medic," Virgilio said.

"Small ones living space bigger ones are supplies, pantry and medic," Gramps translated in English.

"You stay tonight and rest. Tomorrow I will show you to the Japanese lines," Virgilio said in Filipino with a grin.

"Thank you," he replied in Filipino.

"I will stay here tonight and Virgilio will show me the Japanese lines tomorrow morning," he translated.

"I'll stay and fight with Virgilio," Jimmy said with a serious look.

"Where is the radio?" Gramps asked in Filipino.

"It's in the supplies tent. I will radio in that you are here plus one," Virgilio replied in Filipino.

Gramps nodded and Virgilio went off.

"He's gonna radio in that I made it to them with you," Gramps said.

Jimmy scratched his head.

"Ah good I think some sleep is in order don't you think?" he asked. He yawned.

"Yeah sounds good," Gramps replied.

Gramps rubbed his tired eyes. He was amped but at the same time exhausted. He had made it to the Philippines despite the rough flight.

They walked into the tent and fell fast asleep on the ground.
The next morning Gramps woke up and walked out of the hut. He was greeted by Virgilio who was stirring a pot on the fire.
"Come eat," Virgilio instructed and handed him a bowl and spoon.
"Thank you," he said. He filled up the bowl.
"Is Merlin still asleep?" Virgilio asked.
"Yes," Gramps replied. He blew air to cool off his bowl.
They sat down on smooth bamboo made mats on the ground.
The food looked like oatmeal and Gramps took a spoonful of it to his mouth. It sure tasted sweet like it and had bread like taste as well. After he finished the bowl off Virgilio and Gramps walked to the Japanese lines and they parted ways for now.
"Follow the trail up until you get to the clearing, the Japanese camp should be there. You better dirty yourself up a bit," Virgilio said.
"Yeah thanks sounds good," Gramps answered.
"When do you want to meet?" he asked.
"We meet once a week Friday halfway to the camp," Virgilio said.
Gramps nodded.
"What should I do if I need to meet with you earlier?" I asked.
"Come to the campsite and see me," he replied.
"Okay got it," Gramps said. He disappeared back into the dense jungle. Gramps grabbed a handful of dirt and rubbed it on his uniform to make it appear that he had been getting down and dirty fighting for days. He admitted he was really nervous. As he walked to the Japanese lines he greatly feared some sniper was going pick him off. Then, he had all these thoughts in his head you know; what if they didn't believe him, would he be tortured, how long could he last being tortured, or would they just shoot him on the spot? He knew it certainly wasn't the greatest time to be having these thoughts but at that moment he didn't know what was going happen next and that terrified him more than anything. With each step his heart raced faster, the grip on his Thompson became tighter, and he became more agitated than before. He could hear gunfire far off in the distance and the distinct pinging sound as an empty ammo clip of a U.S. M1 Garand rifle ejected echoed thought out the jungle. A few minutes later he came face to face with an armed Japanese patrol.

"I surrender!" Gramps said in Japanese. He held up his Thompson for them to take.
"You speak Japanese?" the squad leader asked in Japanese. He hunched forward and he scowled.
"Yes, I do," Gramps coolly replied in Japanese with his hands still up.
"You intelligence?" He screamed in an angry voice in Japanese still scowling.
As Gramps turned his head around he saw the other two Imperials stood there at the ready with their weapons trained on him. As he made eye contact with them their facial expression didn't change they seemed tight and had real serious looks. Their fingers on the triggers and their bayonets shined in the sunlight.
"No, translator," Gramps answered in Japanese. He acted frightened.
As Gramps held his hands up the squad leader threw his head to the side and two of the other soldiers relieved him of his weapons. One, took his Tommy, another took his .45 pistol and the others had their bolt action Arisaka rifles at the ready equipped with sharp bayonets on them. The rifles themselves were bolt action meaning that you had to manually eject the shell of the spent round by pulling the bolt back. After that two of the men stayed in the back and the other three were in the front as they walked back to their camp. The group walked for another five minutes and then the jungle opened up and there was a small Japanese base camp.
The area was small about the size of a few house lots. Gramps first took notice of how it was surrounded by the jungle on all sides. There also was no other trail that was cleared except the one they were currently on. The Japanese constructed a barracks, a large hut and a barbed wire area compete with a large gate for POWs. The squad leader yelled and soon the entire camp of 25 men came to greet Gramps. Then, the leader of the camp a Captain stood in front of him. The Captain grabbed him and tossed him into a large hut. There were two chairs inside and so when he got back on his feet he sat down on one.
"Name, rank, and place of residency," the Captain demanded.
He walked to a small wooden desk and pulled from the top of it a pen and a pad of paper. He then walked back and slapped them down on the wooden table in front to them.

As Gramps studied him, he seemed tense, too. He pulled his sidearm a Nambu pistol from his holster and placed it on the table, the barrel facing Gramps and he picked up the pen.

"Kinjiro Kabazawa, Sergeant, Kauai, Hawaii," Gramps smoothly answered in Japanese in one breath.

"Kabazawa? Where is your family from?" he asked in surprise. His eyebrows perked up.

"Niigata," Gramps replied.

"Are you related to an army officer who served in the Russo-Japanese War?" he asked, leaning forward over the table.

"Yes, my father's brother," Gramps replied.

"Ah, in the war, your uncle saved my father's life," he said. He leaned back now and relaxed.

"He did?" Gramps leaned forward in disbelief. His jaw dropped and he began to laugh.

"Yes." The man once again sat up straight. "Now what was your duty with the Americans?"

"I was a translator, I can speak fluently in English, Japanese and Filipino dialects," Gramps answered. He now felt relaxed enough to scratch his shoulder.

"Why did you surrender to us?" he asked in a serious tone.

"After Pearl Harbor was bombed, the American troops became hostile towards men, like us. After news of the bombing, a few of them tried to kill me, but I was quicker. After that, I crossed your lines, where I surrendered to the patrol that brought me in to you," Gramps reveled, shifting his weight in his chair.

"The Americans tried to kill you?" he asked, his tone even more serious.

"Yes, but I got them first," Gramps angrily announced.

Grandpa knew he had the Captain - hook, line and sinker - so there was no reason for him to stay uptight. He slouched back into his chair.

"I see," he glared at the Japanese-American 'turncoat' as his face tightened.

Gramps returned to sitting upright.

"And you want to kill more American troops?"

"Why should I fight for a country who wants nothing to do with me? Yes I want to kill Americans!" Gramps said with conviction.

He got up, opened a chest and tossed him a Japanese uniform.
"Welcome to the Imperial Japanese Army, Lieutenant," He bowed to
Gramps.
Gramps quickly stood up, snapped to attention and he returned the bow.
"I will give you a minute to change," he said, and left the hut.
Gramps nodded.
After the Captain left, Gramps began to speak English.
"Holy shit," Gramps whispered to himself aloud with a quiet laugh, "a
lieutenant!"
He wiped the dripping sweat from his forehead and kept laughing.
After Grandpa's excitement had quieted down, he let out a sigh of
overwhelming relief, but the true test was about to being. Still, he was in a
shock that the cover story worked! He changed into the Japanese combat
uniform and went outside. The captain formally presented to him a Nambu
pistol and a Samurai sword. When the short ceremony was over, Gramps
was personally introduced to all of the men. Many of the men were quite
young; 17, 18, 19, at the most their early twenties. He learned that Sato, the
captain was about 30 and Hiroto, the sergeant who brought him in was 33.
From the moment he was introduced to a private named Ichiro, Gramps
could see it in his eyes that he aroused the Private's suspicions. However,
Gramps outranked him and had the Captain in his pocket. There was another
lieutenant by the name of Kiyoshi but he didn't seem to pay much attention
to anything but the food. He was a heavy set guy whose only care was to
satisfy his appetite. He was 22 years old.
As the week rolled on, Gramps became much closer to the men. Most of
them wanted to know about Hawaii and the fishing, so he told them tales.
Hell, he even taught Sato how to speak English, at his request. To avoid
suspicion, Gramps took night walks around the jungle every night and
always managed to do so unseen, or so he thought.
"What were you doing?" Ichiro demanded, scowling at Gramps.
"I just came back from a walk," Gramps replied.
"Why?" he asked skeptically.
"Because it reminds me of home, and I like nature. I like being alone to
think," Gramps answered.
He walked up closer to Gramps.

"Lier!" he shouted in Grandpa's face. "You have been talking with the enemy haven't you?" he glared and stuck his finger in Grandpa's chest as if it was a gun.

"No, I have not! Private Ichiro, don't ever accuse me of that again. Remember I outrank you. If you forget, I will have you punished for insubordination!" Gramps swatted away Ichiro's hand and gave him a good shove.

Ichiro slid backwards and caught his balance in the nick of time. A slight second later he would have been on the ground.

"Yeah, yeah," he snarled and walked away.

"Get back here, Private!" Gramps yelled. He stomped a foot on the dirt. By the time he turned around and walked back to Gramps, they had an audience.

His manner was insolent. "What do you want?"

Gramps toll the tone of an Imperial Officer, "You may not like the man, Private Ichiro, but you will respect his rank!" Gramps laid one hand on his holster, ready to skin it, and then he stepped right into Ichiro's face.

Grandpa screamed like a drill instructor. "You got that, *Private*?"

"Yes, Lieutenant Kabazawa!" he shouted. He stepped back and bowed to Gramps.

Gramps returned the bow. "You are dismissed, Private!" Ichiro returned to his quarters.

Grandpa felt the veins in his neck popping out, visible to anyone who looked. He was sure his face was red with fury, but it fed the bluff. As an Imperial officer, Grandpa deserved respect!

"You are too easy on him, Kabazawa." Captain Sato remarked. He'd watched the whole thing unfold.

"Why what you would have done?" Gramps asked. He pull up into attention.

"I would have struck him until he fell and then kicked him a few times while on the ground." Cap Sato said.

Now Gramps relaxed. "Ah well I just want to make sure I don't get shot in the back."

"Yes, I understand." Sato scratched his cheek. "But there always be that one person no matter what you do, who will always be irked by you. You must be hard on such men."

He pulled from his hip pocket out a pack of smokes and a lighter. He took out one cigarette and turned the open pack to Gramps. He waved it away. He nodded, put the pack away, lit his cigarette, and slid the lighter back in his pants pocket.

Gramps confessed, "I just want to know that I can trust the men. I want to know for a fact that they won't shoot me in the heat of battle."

Sato took a thoughtful drag on his cigarette. "Trust is a tricky thing," he agreed, Even more so in war." He exhaled a cloud of smoke. It hung in the air like the question of Grandpa's safety from Ichiro and anyone else he inflicted with his suspicions and "lies."

"Yeah it sure is."

"Nevertheless, I will talk with Ichiro, straighten him out, and make sure this never happens again. Besides, I do not want a munity the next time we are under fire, " he said

Gramps nodded. "Thank you, Sato."

He exhaled another cloud of smoke.

"You are welcome." He exhaled another plume of smoke, holding the cigarette between his thumb and forefinger like Bogart in the movies, and he walked away.

In that moment, Gramps thought what a shame it would be if his cover was blown and he should ever have to kill Sato. He wasn't as cruel as the other men, but Gramps suspected Sato had a side of him that was cruel. He had yet to see it. Gramps meant, Sato was a good man, maybe an honorable man, but like any of these men, he wouldn't hesitate to kill him as a spy.

To calm his nerves of living the dual life as a spy he began to drink. There were many large wooden crates of sake, Japanese rice wine. He would drink on the go with it mixed with water in his canteen. He would drink with the men at dinner time. He would also drink in his quarters at night. He drank to calm his nerves and it worked. However, his choice in coping would become disastrous later on. For now, though drinking worked.

Besides American soldiers at Bataan and a suspicious Japanese Private, there was an assortment of natural critters that God had sent to the party in the Philippines. Snakes in particular, and a shitload of other fun unfamiliar creatures, just waited to whack him out in the jungle they call home.

As the day came to meet with Virgilio, deep in the jungle on a night lit by the light of a half moon, Gramps expressed his fears to him but the guerrilla leader simply shrugged them off saying that it was because he was a rookie and that it was inexperience that fueled his paranoia.

"Rookie worries, give it time and it will pass," Virgilio brushed off. Gramps scoffed and paced around.

"Easy for you to say you don't got 25 people willing to kill him at a moment's notice!" Grandpa vented.

"I may not have 25 people but I do have one, my wife," he reveled with a short laugh.

"You, you have a wife? You never told me that," Gramps stammered and walked closer to him.

"Would it have made a difference if I did?" he posed. He looked at the sky then back to Gramps.

"No, not really," Gramps replied and laughed.

Gramps put his arm around Virgilio's shoulder.

They laughed about it in the jungle and Gramps glanced up in the sky to look at the stars.

"Wow," Gramps whispered.

"Oh yes it really is a beautiful night. Big difference from last night," he remarked. He caught Gramps.

"Yeah I know. It was filled with clouds. So, how's Jimmy?" Gramps asked. He came back to Earth but his eyes still transfixed at the bright sky.

"He's eager but like many afraid," Virgilio answered.

"Yeah, that does sound like him," Gramps replied. He turned back to him.

"He is slowly picking up on words," Virgilio said.

"Is he now?" Well, that's good news," Gramps said still dazed by the natural beauty of the night.

After the small talk was over Gramps dove right into the information that he was to pass on to him. He told him about the soldier and Captain Sato. He went in great detail on the layout of the camp and the condition of the two American POWs being held there. Virgilio didn't utter a single world but just sat there and soaked it all up until he was done.

"You must find a way to keep everyone else on your side and convince them that there is no doubt of you," he said seriously.

"And how the hell am I supposed to do that?" Gramps asked.

"Well, you're already in and cozy with the top. Just concentrate on strengthening trust and friendships with the rest of the men. It's quite crucial that the men trust you so much that they are willing to die for you," he said.

"So, I drink and joke with them and the doubt will just go away?" Gramps asked.

"Yes and when it does then you can plant your own seeds of doubt and have them turn on each other," he said.

"Ah I like the way you think," Grandpa remarked.

"Yeah. Just keep playin' actor and everything will be all right," he said with a grin.

Gramps nodded.

After they had talked for a few hours the duo parted ways and Gramps zigzagged his way back to camp. It was a nice walk back especially because there was not a cloud in the sky. It reminded Gramps much of home wondering on trails only lit by moonlight in Kokee. Once he got back to camp, went inside his hut and took several large swigs from a sake bottle.

Then after his nightly drinking session he went to sleep.

Some days later Gramps found out about Roosevelt relocating thousands of Japanese and Japanese Americans from the coast states and Hawaii. The Japanese would be put in camps out in isolated areas in the United States. Only the Japanese were picked publicly, privately however some Germans and Italians were also being relocated. The Japanese were given minutes to gather up all the things they could carry and shuttled off to the unknown. As a result, many of them who owned restaurants and other businesses were lost and vandalized. Men, women, children, and the elderly were held against their will for the duration of the war.

The camps had barbed wire fences and large guard towers all around. Machine guns pointed inwards instead of outwards became synonymous with the internment camps. The Canadian and British Governments followed suit detaining Canadian Japanese, British Japanese and Japanese immigrants. Like in the U.S. the Canadians and English, would hold them until the war was over. These decisions would later be called as one of the most shameful in the history of the United States, Canada and Great Britain.

Grandpa was probably the only Japanese American in the world who understood the reason Roosevelt did the internment but it still enraged the hell out of him. He now feared that the Imperials could use the interment as a propaganda tool to recruit Japanese Americans and Japanese nationals in all these nations to spy for them. His greatest fear was that they would be able to convince other Japanese American GIs in the Pacific to join their side. If the Imperials were successful he believe his cover would most definitely be blown.

In early May after the Japanese were victorious in the Battle of Corregidor, they now had full control over the Philippines. Besides some American GIs who joined Filipino guerrillas and those who escaped, thousands of Americans were now POWs at the mercy of the Imperial Japanese whom mercy seemed like a foreign concept to. A few days later they received 10 more American POWs. Gramps and the camp's Imperials were not part of the Bataan Death March but that didn't mean that the Americans wouldn't suffer hell.

The Americans were subjected to torture that tested them physically and mentally to the breaking point and beyond. Gramps witnessed the brutality of all of it first-hand but he had no part in it whatsoever. Starvation, beatings, being stretched out by rope, and many other torture methods were used. Some of the men broke quickly while others took time but in the end all 12 POWs broke after be subjected to torture. After more than 60 years he still could not get those images out of his head.

Chapter 4

Da Great Pacific Treasure Hunt

As the months rolled by Gramps gained the trust and respect of Private Ichiro and it was all smooth sailing. Sato gave him the job of playing good cop to the American POWs to gain any other pieces of information they were still holding. In his talks with them he found out that they were from all different parts of the Continental U.S. For example three of the men were from small towns in Ohio, South Dakota, and Rhode Island. Other places the men hailed from were New York, New Jersey, Colorado, Arkansas, Utah, Kansas and Texas. He didn't reveal to them that he was a spy for the Americans because he knew they would give him up when they would be grilled by the Imperials. They did divulge to him things such as the location of hidden weapons caches inside caves and the names of buddies of theirs who had evaded capture. He gave nothing to Sato but old information that he knew they already had such as troop movements. Since, the POWs had been in captivity by them for some time Sato didn't really expect the POWs knew much current stuff anyway.

Gramps told Virgilio about the hidden weapons caches and they soon went to search for them. They found the caves and a vast array of American hardware. Machine guns, rifles, handguns and grenades were recovered and were now in the hands of guerrillas. He ended up bonding with the American POWs by the way of sports and trading tales of home. Grandpa's role was basically to soften them up so that went they would be interrogated by Hiroto as the bad cop they would give up intel easily.

By November Sato had become fluent in English and he was now conducting the bad cop interrogations. After months of a cozy lifestyle inside the camp Gramps was now ordered by Sato to go out and lead a small unit. His mission was to search the multitude of caves and locate treasures the Filipinos had hidden away. What he didn't know at the time was that in all of the conquered lands the Japanese were looting and creating massive treasure hoards. Artwork, jewelry, currency, precious metals, and hell even statues they took it all. Later in the war the treasure hoards would be combined to form the legendary mega hoard called Yamashita's Gold or Yamashita's Treasure. The mega treasure hoard took its name from a Japanese Imperial General Tomoyuki Yamashita. Yamashita had made a name for himself for attacking and taking control over Malaya and Singapore in 1941 and early 1942. He was placed in command of the Fourteenth Area Army in the Philippines from 1944 until the wars end in 1945. After the war he was tried, convicted and executed for war crimes by the Tokyo War Crimes Tribunal in 1946.

So, now here Gramps was in control of a unit and all he could think about was hoping not to run into any resistance. The way he saw it he had two choices if they ran into guerrillas, one was to kill the good guys thus preserving his cover and distinguishing himself even more among the men. The other choice was to kill the Japanese unit and surrender to the guerrillas in the hope that it was Virgilio's men. Finally, after hours of cave searching they took around a hundred pounds of treasure from 15 caves and made their way back to camp. One of the treasures was inside a small chest that one would find on a pirate ship. The chest was loaded with treasure and the rest of the loose stuff that they found the men put them in bags as they continued their search. The unit got back to camp just as the sun was setting. He could breathe a sigh of relief that they were not engaged in their search for artifacts.

"What have you found?" Sato asked, quite eager as they arrived back at camp.

"Take a look for yourself," Gramps replied and unlatched a chest.

"Wow!" He exclaimed with a big smile. He stared at the contents of the chest.

The chest was filled with jewelry and precious stones that included emeralds, rubies, and diamonds.

"Good job men, dismissed!" Sato said all smiles. He closed the chest up. The men bowed and went to get some hot chow. They ate horse meat and clowned around until Gramps left to do his nightly walk. 15 minutes after zigzagging through the dense jungle he met with Virgilio and they got down to business.

"Sato sent me out with a unit to find treasures that you guys and the Americans hid," Gramps said. He pulled out his canteen and drank from it.

"You find anything?" he asked. He slapped his neck, killing a mosquito.

"Mmm, yeah, we did. Sato is holding it," Gramps replied. He swallowed.

"We must find a way to retrieve it," Virgilio stated. He scratched his head.

"Yeah I know hopefully before they decide to move it somewhere safer," Gramps remarked. He put his canteen away.

Virgilio nodded.

"You run into any fighters while on the search?" he asked, concerned.

"No, and I prayed I wouldn't," Grandpa confessed.

"Yes well I suppose the man upstairs was listening," Virgilio quipped.

Gramps laughed.

"I guess so. I know how I can smuggle the treasure to you," Gramps said.

"How?" he intrigued asked.

"The men haven't recorded the loot so all I would have to do is pocket some before they do and hand it off to you," Gramps said with a smile.

"That would work, just don't get caught," he replied and placed his hand on Grandpa's shoulder.

"Yeah, yeah I know," Gramps said annoyed.

"How are the Americans?" he asked.

"Not so good. They are bone skinny but I have been keeping their spirits up by swapping stories of home," Gramps said.

"Don't get too close," Virgilio sternly warned.

"Shit, I don't see how I couldn't," Gramps replied.

"This war will not only take the lives of people but it will also take the souls of the living. Those not killed will be cold and soulless. You Kinjiro still have your soul but the question remains is for how long?" he stated deeply.

"Well, let's hope for both our sakes I don't ever find out," Gramps answered lightly.

He nodded.

"Is that all?" He asked.

"Yes, for now," Gramps replied.

"Good I shall see you later," he said.

"See you later," Gramps replied.

After that the duo parted ways and as a wave of clouds covered the moon Grandpa decided to take out his flashlight before he would stumble in the darkness. Once he got to camp he checked on the chest which was still in Sato's possession and he went to bed. The next morning before everyone else was awake he snuck out a few artifacts from Sato's chest and several loose items from the loot. He hid them with his stuff and went back to sleep.

As he tried to go back to sleep his heart raced so much it became unbearable. So, he quickly gave up and pretended to be asleep while everyone was waking up.

As the day progressed Gramps became aware that Sato didn't even notice that there were things missing from the chest. As a matter of fact it would be early January 1943 before he even opened it up again. To his amazement Sato didn't even know anything was missing from it in January. By Friday Gramps met again with Virgilio and gave him some of the loot. He informed the guerrilla leader that the rest of the treasure had been cataloged down and the log book was in Sato's tent. The loose pieces that Gramps gave him included a painting from the 18th century, a golden cross with a large ruby on it and a golden cross necklace. The stuff from the chest included a bunch of rings and various coins.

"Can you bring me more artifacts?" he asked.

"No, not without arousing suspicion or risking my cover," Gramps said.

"Okay," he replied.

"So, how's Jimmy?" Gramps asked.

"Oh he's good his language skills are near fluent," Virgilio said.

"Really? That's great news!" Grandpa commended.

"Yeah, he is a great fighter and entertains the kids with stories of his home," he said.

"Ah yes, home," Gramps replied.

In that instant Grandpa thought of home and how much everything has changed or hasn't. He began to have flashbacks of home and as he closed his eyes he could smell the cows. He worked at the Waimea Dairy milking cows and so everything began to come back to him. He had thought of home before but this time it was different. He began to long for that familiar voice of his Mom and that salt breeze air of Kauai. And he swore in that moment he made a vow that he would get home alive to his island and his Mother.

The only problem was that he had no idea when that was to be.

"Kinjiro are you alright?" Virgilio asked.

"Yes, I'm just reminiscing of home," Gramps confessed. He opened his eyes.

"Good. Remember them and those moments because that is what you are fighting for. Never let that voice or that picture fade away," he stated.

"I won't," Gramps confidently replied.

"Good because we have a goddamn war to win," he remarked.

"Damn right," Gramps said.

After that motivational speech they parted ways and Gramps went back to the camp. All along the walk back he thought in his head that the thing that had driven him up until that moment, proving himself to everyone.

When his drive, his will to fight and carry on should have been home because if he failed it would be all gone. So, now his drive was to preserve and protect the thing that mattered most to him, home. He wasn't fighting for the United States, for President Roosevelt, for the agents, or for some top General no, he was fight to go back to the life he used to have. He was fighting for the people and the places that made it up.

'Relish in those moments because you never know how or when they can end up saving you.' Gramps thought.

If it wasn't for that conversation with Virgilio, Gramps didn't know if he would have ever made it through. However, the real test was soon to come and it would bring him to people and places he never thought possible.

Chapter 5

Blown Outta The Water

In early January 1943 Grandpa's cover was nearly blown completely and everyone's nerves would be put to the test. A few days after celebrating New Year's 1943 he met with Virgilio, unknown to him at the time was that Ichiro, the suspicious Japanese Private had decided to follow him. Gramps assumed it was partially his fault for not zigzagging around as much. He used to lose any tail he had.

Ichiro, that bastard was a smart one though because rather than bust Gramps straight out he waited and gather enough evidence to nail him to the wall. The PFC waited and watched him for two weeks before he said anything. That sneaky son of a bitch! About two weeks later after Gramps met with Virgilio he got back to the camp and all the men were up and waiting for him.

"What the hell are you doing out there?" Sato flipped out.

"I was just meeting with a friend," Gramps replied. He showed no emotion.

"Lier! You think we are fools! I followed you into the jungle and saw your meeting! SPY!" Ichiro yelled and pointed a finger at Gramps.

With all eyes on Gramps and now guns trained on him, he knew he had to come up with something good and fast.

"I AM NOT A SPY!" Gramps screamed angrily at Ichiro and stomped his feet.

"That man I was meeting was my contact in the guerrillas you stupid idiot!" Gramps blurted out in anger. He walked closer Ichiro.

"You have a contact?" Sato surprised asked.

"Yes, and he is loyal to the Japanese," Gramps reveled. He panted.

"Lower your weapons," Sato ordered. He put his hand in the air.

As the men lowered their guns Gramps could still sense that they still didn't believe it.

"Come Kinjiro let us talk in private." Sato said. He waved his hand to Gramps.

Gramps nodded and walked with him. As Gramps passed Ichiro they locked eyes and glared at each other. Sato led Gramps to his quarters and they got right down to it.

"I want to meet him, your contact," Sato ordered in English.

"Sure when?" Gramps asked in English.

"Tomorrow during the daylight," he instructed. He paced around.

"Okay I'll have to let him know. It may take a bit of time to convince him so I may come back in the morning," Gramps replied. He tapped the table rhythmically with his fingers.

"All right sounds good go now," he replied, convinced.

Gramps nodded and began walking to Virgilio's camp.

To say Grandpa was nervous was a gross understatement he was fuckin' terrified! He thought for sure this was it you know Virgilio was going come into the camp tomorrow and they both would be killed. People always tell you to stay positive and shit like that but he was sure that they wouldn't if their neck was stretched out like this. Gramps was trained and had been under pressure before but now it was at the point that both he and Virgilio could be killed in an instant. When Gramps got to the camp he was greeted by a familiar face one whom he hadn't seen since parachuting down in the jungle.

"Jimmy," Gramps said.

"What the hell are you doin' here kid?" Jimmy surprised asked.

The duo hugged each other and then Grandpa answered his question.

"How the hell are ya Jimmy?" Gramps asked.

"Alive. What do you need?" He said.

"I need to talk to Virgilio. My cover is fucked," Gramps said.

"Oh shit! So, what's the plan?" he asked, eagerly.

"Uh I don't know right now. One of the men caught me meeting with him in the jungle a few times and called me out on it so I told them that I

was meeting my guerrilla contact who was loyal to the Imperials," Gramps
said.

"Ah and they want a meet," he inferred.

"Yeah, pretty much," Gramps answered.

"All right follow me," he said.

Jimmy led him into one of the huts and there sat Virgilio cleaning his
rifle.

"What are you doing here?" Virgilio asked in Filipino.

"We have a problem," Gramps said.

Jimmy explained the situation to Virgilio and then trio came up with a
game plan.

Since recovering many American weapons plus captured Japanese ones
as well the guerrilla fighters had quite a bit of firepower. The plan they
devised was that Virgilio and Gramps would head into the Japanese Camp
the next morning. At the same time Jimmy along with many of the fighters
would surround the camp and remain hidden by the dense jungle that
surrounded the area. He would wait with a pair of binoculars until Gramps
gave the signal and then they would open fire on the camp from all sides. In
the firefight Virgilio and Gramps would get out as many of the American
POWs as they could while the rest of the Japanese were occupied with the
fighters. It seemed like a good plan but they all knew how that could change
into a major disaster in a heartbeat.

No plan is ever foolproof, especially one as daring as this one so they all
agreed that if anything should happen to Virgilio or Gramps not a single
Japanese solider would survive.

"All right so do we understand the plan?" Gramps asked. He looked
around at Jimmy and Virgilio.

Everyone nodded in agreement.

"I will brief the fighters. I will also send a message out to Roosevelt on
the situation," Virgilio said. He stood up.

Gramps nodded.

"Aren't the Japanese expecting you back tonight?" Jimmy asked.

"No, so I'll be spending the night here," Gramps smiled.

Jimmy laughed.

"Just like old times," he remarked.

"Yeah, has it really been that long?" Gramps said with a chuckle.

"The kid that I saw makin' a snow angel on the ground seems like a lifetime ago. Looks to me that the kid has been replaced with the man I see now standing before me," he remarked and placed his hand on Grandpa's shoulder.

"Yeah, where the hell did that kid go, huh?" Gramps asked.

After that Grandpa decided to get some sleep before the big day tomorrow. Jimmy led him to a hut and Gramps just passed out.

The next morning Virgilio woke Gramps up at 8AM. He informed him that Jimmy had taken the fighters to get into position two hours earlier and that they had decided to let him sleep.

"It didn't make sense to wake you so early so we just let you rest," Virgilio explained as they ate breakfast.

Breakfast was a kind of chicken stew or soup which Gramps found out from Jimmy that it was leftovers from last night's dinner. It was later that Gramps found out that the meat in the stew was not of chicken but of monkey! He didn't mind it one bit because as far as he was concerned his time in the Pacific would be over soon and he would be able to go home.

After they finished breakfast the duo set out to the Japanese camp.

"I sent the message last night and got a reply this morning. Roosevelt knows that if we kill every Imperial in the camp and stay under then there is a good chance that you will receive a posting of your choice. He wants you to choose Denmark which is coming as a request from the British," Virgilio said.

"Wait, what? Roosevelt wants me to stay under? The hell with that I'm going home. Or better yet tell Frankie to get his old crippled ass over here!" Gramps grumbled.

Virgilio grabbed Grandpa's arm and he stopped dead in his tracks.

"We have a chance to end this war won't you do it?" he posed. He looked Gramps square in the eyes.

They stood there staring right at each other and Gramps let out a heavy sigh. After a moment to collect his thoughts Gramps came up with an idea.

"All right I have an idea. Follow my lead and don't ever question me," Gramps said.

With a grin on his face Virgilio nodded and they continued on their way to the Japanese Camp. Once the duo got to the camp one of the men fetched Sato. Sato came along with Ichiro and Gramps informed Sato that he would act as translator. After introductions the men went to Sato's quarters for a more private discussion.

"I am honored to have finally met you Commander," Sato said in Japanese with a smile.

Gramps translated word for word to Virgilio. They chatted for a half hour and then Gramps excused himself for a cigar.

"I didn't know you smoke." Sato said in English.

"Yeah, I uh just started," Gramps replied.

"Ah yes very well," he responded with a half-smile.

Gramps went outside and took a small box of matches along with a large cigar from his pocket. He struck the back on the box and lit his cigar. He took a few puffs and exhaled large gray clouds of smoke. Right after the exhale of clouds the jungle lit up with heavy automatic gunfire as that was the signal. He pulled his sidearm the Nambu pistol that they had given him when he "surrendered" to them and shot three of the men around. Most of the men were firing at the fighters in the jungle while Virgilio and Gramps were taking on the rest. He heard Virgilio open up on Sato and Ichiro with a .45 pistol. As Gramps heard footsteps from behind him, he hastily turned with his pistol at the ready. Virgilio emerged unharmed from Sato's quarters.

"Are they dead?" Gramps asked.

"With a round to the head each," he replied.

He tossed Gramps a Tommy gun and they continued on the way through the camp. As bullets whizzed through the place Virgilio and Gramps made it to the POW holding area he shot the two guards and Gramps freed the Americans. While exchanging gunfire with the Imperials all but two of the American soldiers were killed. Within 20 minutes after Gramps had signaled Jimmy to open fire the battle was over. All of the Imperials in the camp were dead along with ten of the American POWs and eight fighters. 15 fighters were wounded and after the all clear was given Jimmy and the rest of the fighters came into the camp.

"Well the area is secure. What now Ken?" Jimmy asked in English.

"Phase two," Gramps replied. He ejected an empty mag and replaced it with a fresh one.

"I'll message in that your cover is intact and forward your plan," Virgilio said.

"What plan?" Jimmy asked in Filipino confused.

"After we secured the camp Virgilio would message in that we had succeeded in doing so and that I was still alive. There will be an Imperial unit to visit the camp later tonight to check in case anything went wrong," Gramps said. He pulled out his canteen.

"Sato's insurance," Jimmy said. He pieced it all together.

Gramps nodded and drank.

"Yeah so after you guys take treasures and intelligence papers from the camp Virgilio or perhaps you will crack me with a sidearm behind the head. When I wake up later tonight I will have the perfect cover story I got knocked out during the fighting." Gramps finished and put his canteen away.

He chuckled.

"You think they'll buy that?" he asked. He crossed his arms.

"Well, they already bought one bullshit story, why not another?" Gramps asked with a sly grin.

"Fair enough. So, what you wake up, feed them the tale and ask for a new posting?" he stated.

"Yeah pretty much. And by the sounds of it they want me in Jerry country," Gramps replied with a grin.

"Shit you know who's right below Denmark right?" he exclaimed.

"Yeah Germany. And the fact that the Krauts have been occupying it since the 9th of April 1940 is even worse," Gramps replied.

"They sure know how to pick 'em." he said with a smile.

"Oh yeah," Grandpa replied and chuckled.

Just then Virgilio came back with a sheet of paper and gave it to Gramps. The guerrilla leader informed Gramps that it was further instructions and that his plan was approved. As Gramps scanned the paper his eyes started to get bigger and he could feel his heart begin to race another marathon.

"What does it say?" Jimmy asked anxiously.

"The message was sent by Winston Churchill, the Brit Prime Minister. He wants me to choose Denmark as my new posting. It also states that he wants to meet face to face to personally brief me," Gramps said. He pulled his head out of the paper.

"Does it say where he wants to meet?" Jimmy asked. He scratched his head.

"Yeah uh Casablanca." Gramps read off.

"Virgilio is this right?" Gramps asked in Filipino and rubbed his eyes.

"Yeah it is," Virgilio answered.

"Casablanca? You know I got a cousin of mine in North Africa. Yeah, he's one of Patton's boys manning a .50 Cal on a Sherman," Jimmy said. He cracked his knuckles.

"Really? What's his name?" Gramps asked, surprised.

"Uh it's Kevin and I believe he's a Sergeant," he replied.

"Oaky so are you ready?" Virgilio asked. He checked his weapon.

"You already took the stuff?" Gramps asked. He cracked his neck.

"Yeah we're hauling it back as we speak," he answered. He looked to the men pulling stuff out of Sato's quarters.

Gramps nodded and the three of them walked outside and they spoke one last time.

"I'll see you around Kinjiro," Jimmy said in English as we hugged.

"Yeah see you around." Gramps replied as he patted his back in the hug.

"It's been swell," Virgilio said with a thick Filipino accent in English.

"Yes it has Virgilio," Gramps replied in English as they hugged.

"Thank you very much," he said with his thick Filipino accent in English.

"You're welcome," Gramps replied with a half grin.

The two men stood in front of Gramps and gave a crisp salute. He returned it and Virgilio got in back of Gramps with a .45 out ready to knock him upside the head. Jimmy stood in front of Gramps and they had one last conversation together.

"You know I never got to thank you for savin' my ass and being a wonderful friend. So, I'll say it now thank you for everything," he said with a grin.

"You are very welcome and thank you for being a great buddy. When the war's over I'll look you up and we'll get together," Gramps said.

"I like that sounds like a plan buddy. Yeah and toss back a few," he answered with a smile.

Gramps chuckled, nodded at Jimmy and turned around and nodded at Virgilio. The last thing he saw was Jimmy's face before everything went black and he crumpled to the ground unconscious.

Chapter 6

Farewell Philippines

When Grandpa began to wake up he could hear voices faintly speaking Japanese and he guess he must have groaned loudly because the voices began to get closer. By the time he rolled over and opened his eyes he saw three figures standing over him. As his vision got back to normal he saw that they were indeed Imperial Japanese Army soldiers. As the three soldiers helped him to his feet, one of them called their commanding officer a Major over to them. Once the Major walked over Gramps explained to him that they had gotten ambushed and he sometime in the beginning of it was knocked out.

"Well you are very lucky Lieutenant Kabazawa," he stated in Japanese.

A day later after the commotion about the ambush had died down Gramps was given a choice for his next posting from the Japanese. To his amazement there was no investigation and no one questioned his story. Nor did anyone question where he chose for his next posting. He wasn't hailed a hero because he had been knocked out during the battle but he wasn't condemned a coward for it either. It was more like the Imperials wanted to reward him for surviving and for the intel he had gotten out of the American POWs from his camp.

"Wait so that it? I mean they never question you some more?" I asked.

"Nope. I was the only one left standing. And even if they did poke around the evidence would back me," Gramps said.

At the same time however they wanted to sweep Gramps under the rug because he had not distinguished himself in combat for them. As enraged he was he knew he wouldn't have been able to kill Americas. No, he just wanted to deck them but not kill them. If he had to shoot at them he would shoot to wound not to kill. On patrol with other Japanese soldiers though he would do the same, shoot to wound not to kill. If anyone would question him, he would reply that enemy soldiers were going to be POWs and they could get vital intelligence out of them.

The last night Grandpa was in the Philippines one of the high-ranking officers decided to throw him a little party and had a Filipino woman in his tent for him. History shows that the Japanese committed numerous war crimes during the war of which included mass rapes. The woman could have been in her early twenties or late teens. Her clothes were torn and soiled and it looked like that she hadn't had a bath in a while. She was skinny despite it all she had a beautiful face with jade green eyes. She was just used for sex by the Japanese soldiers and tossed aside. She also had long jet black hair that Gramps suspected were filled with lice. As he sat down next to her he could tell that she was broken down to nothing because she didn't whimper or even make a sound.

Gramps conversed with her in Japanese but there was no change in her expression so he decided to try in Filipino. As soon as he switched to Filipino she looked directly at him and her face lit up.

They conversed for hours and Gramps began to notice that life began to come back to this poor broken women. He found her name was Sarah and that her family was killed by Japanese soldiers. Sarah was constantly subjected to rape and abuse since her capture in 1941.

"You better lie down next to me in case anyone decided to sneak a peek," Sarah suggested.

"Good idea," Gramps replied with a nod.

Grandpa noticed that she kept rubbing her arms to get warm so he unzipped his duffle bag and pulled out a jacket. The jacket he had pulled out was his U.S. Army one and it was part of the dress uniform.

"Here to stay warm," he said. He handed her the jacket.

"Thank you. You an American?" she asked. She noticed the jacket.

"Yes, I'm uh an undercover agent," he replied with a wink and grin.

Sarah's eyes lit up again and this time it was brighter than before. She longed for the day that she would be free of her oppressors but feared that it would come too late or perhaps not at all.

"You are leaving?" Sarah asked intrigued.

Gramps nodded.

"Yes, I'm being pulled out," he answered. He ran his fingers through her hair.

"Take me with you!" She pleaded.

Gramps let out a heavy sigh.

"No, I can't I'm sorry. But I can do you one better," he said with a sly grin.

"What?" she asked really intrigued.

Gramps took a quick glance at his watch then looked back at her.

"In an hour there will be a plane with German markings coming to get me. Most of the attention will be on it. You can use that time to escape and walk west into the jungle. Keep walking west for 25 minutes and then make a right and walk for 10 minutes until you come across a camp. Once there ask for Virgilio and Jimmy tell them that Kinjiro sent you. There you will be safe I promise you that. Here take my watch and compass," he instructed.

Gramps pulled off his watch and pulled out a large compass from his pocket and handed it to her.

"You want your jacket back, Kinjiro?" Sarah asked. She held it.

"No, you keep it. Besides it looks much better on you than it ever did on me," he remarked with a smile.

Sarah smiled and laughed.

Then, she got up and laid right on top of him and rested her head on his chest.

"You know it seemed like a lifetime ago I said these words to anyone, thank you," She said in a soft voice. She stared directly into his eyes.

For a moment Grandpa could feel that she could see right into his soul. The eyes as the saying goes are the windows of one's soul and he knew that she saw his.

"You are greatly welcome," he softly gazed back into her jade green eyes.

Gramps, for the rest of his life swore he hadn't found anyone who had those same beautiful and striking jade green eyes. And coming from someone who had been around as long as he that is really saying something. They just laid there Sarah on top of him and he didn't dare move because it was the first time that they both felt safe and secure. He knew that it was important especially even if only for a short while just to relax and recharge. There she fell fast asleep and he nearly had to do everything in his power to stay awake. When the hour was nearing its end he ran his fingers through her long black hair to wake her up.

"We have to go," Gramps whispered. He ran his thumb down her cheek.

"I know," she whispered back. She slowly opened her eyes.

Sarah got up off of him and he stood up. He helped her up of her feet and they stood there for a moment.

"Kinjiro?" she asked softly.

"Yes?" Gramps said softly.

"Good luck," She said. She leaned closer to his face.

"Same to you," he replied. He leaned in as well.

They kissed and kissed once more.

"So that's what an angel feels like," she whispered and looked into his eyes.

"We really do have to go," he whispered as they kissed one more time.

"All right," she whispered softly back.

After they savored every second of that moment they walked out of the tent. As he looked at the sky the plane was just about to land.

It was March 2012 with memories of Grandpa's war stories of the Pacific swirling in my head I toured the National World War II memorial in Washington DC. I walked through the memorial and saw the Pacific arch. My heart sank because after all this time he still couldn't say he fought in those dense humid tropical jungles. I continued my walk and saw the Atlantic part of the memorial, which takes us to the next part of the adventure.

Chapter 7

God Save The King

The middle school bus dropped me off up the street from Grandma and Grandpa's house I waked in the blistering summer heat to the house. When I got into the house I wiped the sweat off my forehead with my shirt. I saw Gramps sitting at the head of the dining table. He had a tub of Neapolitan and was scooping some into a bowl.

"You hungry?" he said. He held the ice cream scooper in the air.

"Yeah. I'll grab a bowl," I said. I walked into the kitchen.

I grabbed a bowl from the cabinet and walked to the dinner table. I sat on his left. He gave me the scooper and I scooped chunks of ice cream into my bowl. After I was done I got back up and put the tub into the freezer. I retook my seat.

"Damn it's so hot today," I exclaimed. I shoved a large spoonful of the tasty ice cream into my mouth.

"Eh this nothin' compared to North Africa," he said.

"You fought in Africa?" I asked. I stared at him.

He shook his head. "No, not for fight," he said. He shoveled another full spoonful of ice cream into his mouth.

He swallowed his spoonful of ice cream.

"For meeting," he said with a big goofy grin.

"It was after you left the Philippines, right?" I puzzled, asked.

He nodded. "Yeah just after," he said.

When Gramps climbed on the plane to his surprise it was being manned by a single pilot. As he took one last look at the crowd of Japanese soldiers for Sarah but he saw that she was nowhere to be seen so he waved once and ducked in the plane. Then, all of a sudden it began to rain he supposed it was fitting considering his mood at the time. He was sad for Sarah, Virgilio and Jimmy all of whom he was leaving behind him. Though, he still had a smile on his face as they took off into the air. For it was hope that made him grin; yeah the hope that everything would get better and that everyone would be safe. It would be some time before the Germans expected him to land in Copenhagen. Shortly after take-off he pulled his pistol on the pilot and ordered him to fly to Casablanca.

On board the aircraft there were many cans of fuel so that they wouldn't have to land anywhere. Especially, since they were flying over areas that were not the greatest to land. Grandpa's German wasn't that good yet so communications were composed of hand signals and lots of pointing.

Grandpa did disarm him and had control so he guess it worked.

Around this time the war in Africa was raging and it was right in the middle of the Casablanca Conference. As they got closer to Casablanca Gramps radioed in the codename that President Roosevelt had given him so that he wouldn't be shot down above the unforgiving desert.

The Germans and the Japanese had signed an agreement called the Tripartite Pact in 1940 making them allies along with Italy known as the Axis. The Russians also had signed a pact with them as well until it was shattered when the Germans invaded in June 1941 codenamed Operation Barbarossa. To ensure and smooth over any feelings that this would not happen to Japan the Germans set up a secret officers' exchange program. After his heroic actions in Bataan he was tapped to be the first pending on choosing his posting. It appeared that the secret was not so because the Brits knew about it. Although, he would only find out after the war had ended that the German Enigma code machine was broken by the Brits in 1940. The Brits held breaking Enigma a secret for decades.

It was after the war had ended that Gramps found out that he was the first and last candidate of the Japan-Germany officer's exchange program. Once the war was over the records of the secret program fell into U.S. hands where they were all burned to ashes.

"This is Dragon 577, callin' for Sandman 3-4 over," Gramps said over the radio. He wiped the sweat off his face with his sleeve.

After a moment of static over the radio a male voice came over and it had a British accent.

"This is Sandman 3-4; verify code Dragon 577, over," The man ordered.
"03221926, over." Gramps relayed. He cracked his neck.
"Verified. Proceed to Mike 2-6. What are you flying, over?" The man said.
"Acknowledged. Uh I'm flyin' in a plane with Nazi markings on it, over." Gramps replied. He looked at the wing from inside the cockpit.
"Acknowledged. Land in Hanger three, over." the man said.
"Got it, over," Gramps responded. He let out a heavy sigh and scratched his head.

They were in the air for 20 more minutes before they landed in hanger three at the airfield. As they landed a man stood there in the early afternoon sun. He was dressed in a black suit and boy he must have been dying in it. He cradled a Thompson Submachine gun with a drum mag in his arms and a lit cigar dangled from his lips. Gramps opened the airplane door and pushed out the German first. The man on the ground cocked his Tommy and took aim. The German had his hands up in a surrender position and Gramps came out behind with his pistol trained on him. In his other hand Gramps had his duffel bag filled with his stuff.

"I see you got it under control," the man said with a Brit accent. He lowered his Tommy.
"Of course." Gramps replied. He walked out to greet him.
"George." the man introduced himself with his hand out.
"Kinjiro." Gramps replied back as they shook hands.
"Welcome to Casablanca," he said with a smile.
"You were the voice on the radio weren't you?" Gramps asked. He pointed to him.
"Yes, I was Dragon 577," he replied with a grin.
George stood at a staggering six foot two inches and was wearing a black suit with pinstripes. He looked like a gangster. He was skinny but had muscles which were proportional and didn't make him seem bulky.
"Thanks," Gramps replied.
"You uh better get out of that uniform," he suggested.
"Oh, yeah thanks. I have a suit in my bag." Gramps replied. He realized what he was in.
"Good. I got him while you change," he stated and winked one eye at him.

Gramps nodded and went around the other side of the plane with his bag. He hastily changed into his suit and emerged with it. He put on everything but the jacket because it was simply just too damn hot!

"Where's the jacket?" George asked surprised.

"It's in the bag. It's too fuckin' hot brah!" Gramps grumbled.

George let out a sigh of frustration like a disappointed parent.

"Fine, get in the car we're headin' to the hotel. And what the hell is brah?" he said with a face of disappointment.

"Island talk, it means buddy," Gramps replied. He scratched his forehead. The three of them jumped into an army jeep and George drove off. On the drive to the hotel they drove pass a market and the crowds of people buying stuff. As they got closer to the hotel Gramps noticed that the place was swarming with uniformed allied soldiers. After they parked at the hotel George handed over the Nazi pilot to a couple of guys in Allied Military Police. Gramps never saw the pilot again. The duo walked in the lobby of the hotel and George got a key from the front desk.

"This for you. I am right next door. Come on I'll show you your quarters for the next couple of days," George said and Gramps walked with him. They walked up a flight of stairs and a few doors down after that until they hit Grandpa's room.

"Get some rest the meet with Winnie is in four hours," he said a bit more chipper.

Gramps nodded, unlocked the door, walked in and closed the door behind him. He paid no attention to the room but just dropped his bag on the floor and flopped on the bed. It was nearly ten months since Gramps slept in a real bed and so he quickly fell fast asleep among the multiple pillows and warm blankets.

After Gramps awoke up about three and a half hours later, it was nightfall already. He rubbed his eyes and jumped out of bed. All of a sudden he heard someone knocking on his door. He quickly jumped to his feet. He pulled his M1911 .45 pistol and answered the door.

"Whoa – uh do you mind?" George hesitantly, asked. He held up one hand.

"Sorry. What the hell are you doin'?" Gramps asked. He lowered his weapon.

"I came to tell you that the meeting will be in my room. You are welcome to come in and wait until he shows," he said and massaged his shoulder.

"Got it. I'll uh be right over," Gramps replied.

George nodded.

Gramps put on his hip holster, clicked the safety on, and placed it in the holster. He then walked out of the room and into George's next door.

As Grandpa walked in George's room the first thing that caught his eye was that the man had weapons everywhere. He meant hell that Brit had a Tommy next to his bed, a Lee Enfield rifle in the bathroom, and four pistols scattered around the room. He sat at the end of the bed and Gramps joined him.

"So, you got any brothers?" he asked.

"Yeah I got two; an older and a younger, you?" Gramps replied.

"Two, both are older," George replied. He pulled out a pack of smokes and a lighter.

"Ah you're the baby," Gramps remarked with a grin.

"Regrettably so," he replied with a chuckle.

Gramps chuckled.

George pulled one cigarette out of the pack and handed the pack to Gramps. He pulled out one and George lit Grandpa's first then his. After that the Englishman put both the pack and lighter back into his pocket.

"Your older brother where is he serving?" he asked.

"Oh he's not. Nope that bastard is at home. Where are your older brothers?" Gramps answered slightly angry.

"Well, one is a fighter pilot with the Royal Air Force and the other is a Desert Rat fighting in North Africa. The Desert Rats are the British 7th 'Armoured' Division," George reveled. He exhaled a large cloud of smoke.

"Wow." Gramps exclaimed, very surprised. He took a drag of his cigarette.

"So, you got a dame back home?" Gramps asked. He shifted his weight on the bed.

"Yeah, I do," George replied and took out his wallet from his pocket.

George pulled out a small picture out from his wallet and handed it to Gramps. The picture was back and white and the setting was somewhere out doors in the countryside. In the photo it was him and white girl. They had their arms around each other and they looked very happy. The girl was tall, had long hair and was looker for sure.

"Damn. She is beautiful!" Grandpa exclaimed. He handed back the photo.

"Yeah she is. Her name is Amber. This photo was taken in August '39," he said with this big goofy grin.

"Nice yeah we got nothin' like that at home. Hell, come to think of it I don't got a single dame waitin' for me," Gramps remarked.

The duo both had a laugh at that and then someone knocked on the door. They both put out their cigarettes in the glass ash tray and then looked at each other.

George pulled a British made Webley MK VI revolver and went to the door. Gramps pulled his .45 and walked to the door as well.

"On the count of three?" George asked. He looked at Gramps.

"Yeah on three," Gramps answered and nodded.

"One, two, three!" George said and opened the door.

An older white man dressed a suit and hat, yelled as they opened the door with their weapons out and at the ready.

"Goddamn it George!" The man yelled with a British accent and appeared startled.

"Sorry Winnie, but we weren't expecting you early," George apologized and lowered his revolver.

"Yes, well shall we go inside?" Winnie suggested. He tried to brush it off.

George nodded and stowed his revolver back in his holster. Gramps lowered his pistol and put it back in the holster.

"Hello you must be Kinjiro," Winnie said. He stuck out his hand.

"Yes, I am," Gramps replied. They shook hands.

"Sorry, I'm Winston Churchill Prime Minister, Great Britain," he introduced.

"Yes, you are Mr. Prime Minister," Gramps said in awe.

"Was he everything people say he was?" I interrupted.

"Yes, he was right down to that damn hat!" Grandpa smiled and took a sip of his hot coffee.

"Please call me Winnie," Churchill answered. He walked in, took off his hat and sat on the bed.

George and Gramps sat next to him on the bed and the briefing began.

"Kinjiro I see that you have become quite acquainted with George here. For its pretty evident that the American style of shoot now, shoot later has already rubbed off you George. By the way do you have a bottle?" Winnie remarked.

George pulled a bottle out from his bag on the other side of the bed and presented it to Winnie.

"Black label nice," Gramps remarked. He saw the bottle.

"I don't have any glasses so I guess it's straight up," George said and looked at them.

"I see no problem in that. What do you say boys?" Winnie asked. He looked at the youthful duo.

They both shook their heads.

Winnie unscrewed the cap and took a few gulps from the bottle. After he was finished he then handed it to Gramps and he did the same. After Gramps was done he passed it to George and he tossed a few back and then passed the bottle back up the line. Once Winnie got it he placed it back on the night stand. When that was done they got right down to business.

"Now, George here is an agent with the Special Operations Executive. I hand picked him. He operates outside the normal command chain. He answers to me and me alone. Kinjiro, because of your tremendous work in the Philippines all these months I have paired the two of you for a special off the books mission. First of all what do any of you know about the situation in Denmark?" he said. He rubbed his eyes.

"Well, it's deep in occupied Kraut territory. And it is right above Germany," George said. He straightened himself out.

"Hitler invaded Denmark in 1940 and took the country in a matter of hours. The Danes also have a King named Christian the Tenth," Gramps said. He cracked his knuckles.

"Top marks both of you. Shortly after Hitler had invaded Denmark under my orders the British took the Faroe Islands. The islands are not too far away from Great Britain herself and are quite important from a military perspective," Winnie said. He massaged the back of his neck.

"So, how do I come into the picture?" Gramps asked, curiously.

"The problem with Denmark is that we have no proper eyes in the country. I have expressed this to Franklin. And after much pressing that was when he reveled to me about you Ken. Your cover still remains intact and King Christian X wants our help. King George VI of Great Britain has ordered me to place the two of you in Copenhagen, Denmark," he said.

"Wow okay. So, uh what are objectives besides not getting killed or blown?" George asked, intrigued.

At that point they all started to laugh.

"Well, Ken will be in the Danish Nazi office doing paperwork and such. He will be the inside man. He will take everything from the office and funnel that information to you George, and you will relay it to me. Ken your other job will be a middle ground between the British, the Danish Resistance and the Crowns of both Empires. George your job will be to make sure that Ken doesn't get killed and that you are to work alongside the Danish Resistance," Winnie laid out with a yawn.

"Okay so - shit this is more mad than Philippines!" Gramps remarked.

He threw his hand in the air.

"Indeed it is but this is about winning the war and doing whatever it takes to do so," Winnie rallied. He took a large gulp from the bottle.

"I think I need another drink," Gramps remarked.

"I second that," George said with a smile.

Winnie nodded and they passed around the bottle again. After that they talked for more than two hours. The topic of discussion ranged from their homes to their likes of the arts, especially music. It was a chance for all of them to relax for a bit and forget about the war. Being tense all the time doesn't help you need to decompress once in a while or else you'll go mad. They cracked jokes to each other and laughed a bit. It was nice and Gramps felt like he wasn't even in a faraway land in the middle of a massive war. He felt like he was home and comfortable minus the whole desert part but the war felt a million miles away even if only for a moment.

"Well, I'm going to call it a night boys," Winnie stated. He got up from the bed.

They walked with him to the door and then he turned to them to speak once more.

"I will see you both again one final time tomorrow night," Winnie said with a grin.

"Good night Winnie," George and Gramps said at the same time.

"Good night boys," Winnie said as the duo closed the door.

After a moment of silence with the two of them still standing Gramps spoke.

"Well, I gonna call it a night too George," Gramps said and let out a yawn.

"You wanna take the bottle?" he asked. He held it.

"Nah, I got one in my bag," Gramps replied.

He nodded and let out a big smile.

"All right see you in the morning Ken," he said. he stretched and cracked his neck.

Gramps nodded and left.

Gramps walked into his room and sat on the bed. He pulled out a bottle of Sake from his bag and drank straight out of the bottle.

"Holy shit! Winston fuckin' Churchill! What the hell did I get myself into?" Gramps said to himself aloud.

Gramps took a big gulp of Sake and swallowed it. He laid on the bed. He screwed the cap back on and placed the bottle on the nightstand. After that he went to sleep very fast and easily without waking up until later much later.

The Casablanca Conference was at held at the Anfa Hotel in Casablanca, Morocco from 14 January until 24 January 1943. Many of the Allied heads attended from U.S. President Roosevelt, British Prime Minister Churchill along with the heads of Free French Forces General Charles de Gaulle and General Henri Giraud. Josef Stalin the head of the Soviet Union wasn't there due to the Battle of Stalingrad that Soviets were fighting against the Nazis. Hitler had invaded the Soviet Union who was an ally of theirs at the time in June 1941 under Operation Barbarossa. In doing so a new front was opened it was called the Eastern Front and it was mainly between the Soviets and Germans. The Battle of Stalingrad a victory for Soviet Forces and a major turning point in the war for the Allies. It was the first time that the mighty German Army was defeated in battle.

The German defeat at Stalingrad proved that despite it all they were not invincible. So, with the Axis's first defeat the morale for the Allies grew and they began to finally win in what is considered the single deadliest war in modern history. It would be an uphill battle for them and losing many whom they held so dearly but they would prevail in the end.

As Gramps awoke the next morning at around 10:30 AM and he was a bit startled because he forgot that he was in a hotel room in Casablanca. Everything looked different that where he had spent the last ten months in the Philippines. After a moment he realized where he was he started to laugh. Then he abruptly stopped because he came to the realization that if he did that undercover he would be blown. He was dressed in a white tank top and brown colored shorts. He walked next door to George's room and knocked on the door.

"Mornin' Sunshine!" George said, very perky. He opened the door.

"Shut up!" Gramps replied and walked into his room.

"Uggh! You're one of those, a fuckin' morning person!" Gramps grumbled. He rubbed his bloodshot eyes.

"I take it then you're not one?" he said. He closed the door.

"You guessed right, go give yourself a prize," Gramps replied, still a bit annoyed.

George laughed.

"You hungry?" He asked.

"Yeah, let's go out and eat," Gramps suggested with a grin.

"Uh no can do I'm under orders from Churchill to keep you outta sight," George said.

"But I got a plate of food here for ya," he said with a smile.

On the dresser there was a plate of food some kind of meat and some bread. Gramps wolfed it down and washed it all down with some water from a pitcher. After he finished eating breakfast they chatted.

"You ever been in combat George?" Gramps asked. He looked at him.

George nodded.

"I was at Dunkirk. I'm sure you heard of it," he replied. He looked back at Gramps.

George lifted up a cup and saucer loaded with hot tea. The seam rose from the cup and he blew ever so slowly and drank it.

Gramps nodded.

"Yeah that was a fuckin' disaster!" Gramps remarked with no sympathy.

George laughed and set the tea on the nightstand.

"Yeah, it was. I had just gotten over a couple of weeks before the evacuation as a replacement. After that I was tapped by Churchill himself to be his agent in a newly formed outfit called the Special Operations

Executive. SOE deals extensively with sabotage as well as arming and working with various resistance groups. And it's now running spies as well. From the SOE I learned German and most recently Danish," He reveled. He ate a piece of bread from his plate next to him.

"Ah so you did know about headin' to Denmark," Gramps said. He drank some water from the pitcher.

"I suspected something was cooking but I didn't know for sure. As you know I operate on the outside and answer to Churchill directly with no in-betweens," he said. He finished his bread and took a sip of his steaming hot tea.

"Well, that must have gone swell with the other men," Gramps remarked. George chuckled as he set his tea down again.

"Yeah, well none of them knows," he answered. He raised an eyebrow.

The partners ended up talking for hours on all sorts of topics and by nightfall they had gotten to know quite a bit about each other. After a nice hot bath Grandpa got back to George's room with Churchill for the final meeting. Churchill came to the room with a brown paper bag in hand and set in to the dresser. They all sat down on the bed and George pulled out another bottle of Black Label and three glasses this time. George poured the Scotch whisky into their glasses and set the bottle on the ground. After they had their first sip they got down to business.

"Much like the conference that I am here for, you boys are the ones that can make it come true," Winnie stated. He shifted his weight.

"The defeat of the Axis and absolute victory," George stated. Winnie nodded.

"You boys are the thing that will ensure that victory. I know that I don't have to remind you of the stakes, regardless of it I have utter faith and conviction that you will succeed," Winnie stated with conviction.

"Thank you Winnie," George and Gramps said at the same time.

"Ken, for what you did in Operation Trojan, Roosevelt is impressed beyond words. I cannot thank him enough for letting me have you. Ken, welcome to His Majesty's Service and I hereby promote you to the rank of Captain, congratulations," Winnie said. He put his hand on Grandpa's shoulder.

"Wow uh thank you Winnie," Gramps replied speechless. He tapped Winnie's hand.

"You are most welcome," he replied. He retracted his hand.

"George you are promoted to the rank of Major, congratulations," Winnie stated.

"Thank you Winnie," George said. He scratched his head.

"You are most welcome," He replied. He took a tissue out from the box and blew his nose.

"Now, I also have some things for you from SOE. Goodies of sorts," Winnie said with a grin.

Winnie got up, grabbed the brown paper bag he came in with and presented them with the contents of the bag. George and Gramps pulled out everything from the bag which included language books for German and Danish as well as maps of Denmark, two pairs of sunglasses and weapons such as small pistols, silencers and knives.

"Oh yes I almost forgot," Winnie said. He pulled out two rings from his pocket.

"Poison pills?" Gramps asked. He looked at them.

Winnie shook his head.

"Nope hidden inside is a mini compass," he said.

The ring had the design of a Dragon with wings on it made of metal and a blue stone background.

"To open simply rotate the Dragon counterclockwise once around and open it. To lock it simply close it and rotate the dragon clockwise once around, " Winnie instructed. He demonstrated.

Once he opened the ring it revealed a small compass sat inside the secret compartment.

George and Gramps chuckled.

"Right then boys as you know if you get into trouble in Denmark the cavalry won't be coming over the hill to save you. So, this is for you Ken if you get discovered get to a radio, tune it to British Army frequency, and call out Yankee-Pandora-Two – Six- Niner. You know what frequency is the army right?" he said with a serious look.

"Yes, I do. But what does it do?" Gramps asked. He scratched his head.

"Good, remember to say it exactly like that. Once the code is heard ships, aircraft and artillery of His Majesty will all converge fire on your last know location. The Axis must never ever find out about you," he said quite grim.

"So, what about George?" Gramps asked.

"George will fight with the aid of Danish Resistance and make his way back to London," Winnie stated.

"Fuck that! I'm fightin' too!" Gramps angrily vented.

"Ken, you are simply too valuable. I commend you for what you did to preserve your cover in the Philippines but that won't fly deep in occupied Europe," Winnie stated.

"All right, when do we leave?" Gramps asked. He got over it.

"You leave in four hours. Oh and George your Nazi Uniform is waiting for you in the airplane," he said with a grin.

"You can fly?" Gramps asked surprised at George.

"Yeah, it was among the many things I did during my training," he answered. He took a sip from his glass.

"Oh, that works," Gramps remarked.

"Well, I better be leaving," Winnie said. He got up from the bed.

"One for the road Winnie?" Gramps asked.

"Sure boys. Why the hell not!" He replied with a smile.

Gramps got up from the bed, grabbed the bottle, and filled up their glasses full.

"So, what shall we toast to?" George asked. He stood up with them.

After a moment of racking their brains to come up with something Winnie broke the silence.

"To King and County," he stated proudly. He held up his glass.

"To King and Country," George stated proudly. He held up his glass.

"To King and Country," Gramps stated proudly. He held up his glass.

Their glasses make a clinking sound as they hit them together in a toast.

As they drank their glasses they each eyed each other in a playful competition to see who would finish their glass. They chugged down the Scotch whisky with their heads back. The three all drank their glasses dry and set them down on the dresser.

"That is how true men drink," Winnie remarked. He slapped their backs.

"I think I could get used to this," Gramps remarked with a goofy grin. He looked at them.

The trio started to erupt in laughter.

After that was over George and Gramps walked Winnie to the door.

"In all seriousness good luck and Godspeed men. Oh and this mission is called Operation Double Trouble," Winnie said.

"Thank you Prime Minister, sir," George said. He shook hand with Winnie.

"Thank you Prime Minister, sir," Gramps said. He shook hands with Winnie.

After that he waked out and disappeared into the darkness.

"Well, sober up and get packin' we got a war to win," George stated. He slapped Gramps on the shoulder.

"Damn right," Gramps said with a grin.

Gramps walked out of George's room and went next door to his.

As Gramps sat on the bed all he could think about was holy shit I'm heading into Nazi Europe! Just the fact that he was heading to Europe in general was something that he still couldn't wrap his head around. He laid down on the bed. He stared at the ceiling and began to wonder what was going on back home. You know how his parents are and what is happening to his home? He glanced at his watch and decided that it was time to pack.

It didn't take long for Gramps to pack because he hardly took anything out and he was only there for two days. After five minutes of collecting his stuff and placing it in his duffle bag he was finished packing. He laid back down on the bed and stared at the ceiling. He let his mind free and his thoughts dance all around him. He took a deep breath and exhaled as he closed his eyes in the dark of the night.

George would later confess to Gramps that he was so nervous that he couldn't stop shaking. He had seen combat and trained to be a covert agent but Denmark was to be his first mission as a spy. Grandpa supposed they balanced each other out in terms of experience in the field. George had combat experience and Gramps had espionage experience.

"I was wanted to make a difference so when Churchill offered me the position to do so I thought here's my chance and without hesitation I took it," George would later say.

Around this time U.S. forces were locked in fierce fighting against Japanese Imperial Forces in the Guadalcanal Campaign. The island of Guadalcanal is in the Solomon Islands located in the Southwestern Pacific and from August 1942 – February 1943 it was the sight of a massive and bloody battle. Where Grandpa parachuted down in Bataan in the Philippines there were thousands of American and Filipino Prisoners Of War doing slave labor and being starved to death. Many of these men would die before being liberated by U.S. Forces towards the end of the war. Also in the Pacific at this time the Battle of Buna-Gona (November 16, 1942- January 22, 1943) in New Guinea raged on. The battle was with U.S. and Australian Forces against the Japanese and it was part of the New Guinea Campaign.

In the North African Campaign the Battle of Tunisia raged on where it would end in May 1943 as a victory for the Allies. The victory also marked the end of operations in North Africa and the start of the Italian Campaign.

Grandpa couldn't really remember getting up and jumping in the plane to head to Denmark. He was on some autopilot state and it finally wore off sometime in the flight.

"Where the hell are we?" Gramps groggy, asked.

"Uh in the air," George remarked with a chuckle.

"Ohh very funny," Gramps said. He groaned and rubbed his eyes.

George laughed.

"All right we're just over Belgium," George said.

"How long more?" Gramps asked. He walked to the controls.

"A bit. Could you do me a favor?" he asked. He looked at him.

"Sure what?" Gramps asked. He yawned.

"Just talk to me to keep me awake," he said.

Gramps noticed how bloodshot the Englishman's eyes were and how drained he looked. He really did look like hell!

"Got it. Could you teach me German and Danish?" Gramps asked.

George laughed. He turned back to the front.

"Sure, ok uh grab the books that Winnie gave you," he said.

Gramps grabbed his duffle bag that was next to him, unzipped it and pulled out the two books.

"Okay, I got them now what?" Gramps asked with the books in hand.

"Ok, now uh *ficker*," George said. He tried not to laugh.

"*Ficker*," Gramps repeated flawlessly.

George laughed hard.

"Very good," he said. He laughed.

"What is *ficker*?" Gramps asked with a grin.

"Fucker in German," he replied. He turned to Gramps and laughed hard.

They both started to laugh loudly.

"*Ficker*!" George laughed yelled.

"*Ficker*!" Gramps laughed yelled.

The partners would do many more swear words for the rest of the flight. Of course everyone knows that when you begin to learn a new language you always begin with the swear words and George decided to stick with that tradition. Besides foul language George taught Gramps a few greetings in German and Danish.

Chapter 8

Occupied Not Beaten

The duo landed on some military airfield in Copenhagen and there were five or so German troops to greet them.

"Ok, Ken you ready?" George said. He looked at Gramps.

"Yeah, I guess," Gramps replied. He put his game face on.

The door of the plane opened and George and Gramps walked out. The five Germans wore dress SS Uniforms and were all officers. George acted as translator for the introductions and they found out from the Germans that to foil any plan of sabotage and Allied intel they were instructed to treat Grandpa's arrival like normal. There was a car waiting for him and so it gave George the opening he needed to grab the bags of weapons and disappear. He was supposed to meet with Danish Resistance members as soon as possible. He arrived to get settled and relay back to Churchill that they had arrived without incident. As Gramps was driven around the city of Copenhagen he found out that the driver Karl, who spoke better English than him was to be his translator in Denmark.

As Gramps stared out of the window he couldn't hide the big smile on his face nor the astonishment in his eyes as he saw the city from the car.

"It is nice, no?" Karl in English with a thick German accent asked. He looked at Gramps from the car mirror and turned around for just a moment to see his big smile.

"Yeah, it's beautiful," Gramps marveled, in reply.

There was snow everywhere and oh the buildings were beautiful! The buildings were made of stone and other were painted with bright colors.

After 15 minutes of driving around they got into this neighborhood and they stopped outside a large house.

"Where are we?" Gramps asked intrigued.

"This is where you will stay," he stated.

They got out of the car and Gramps with his duffle in hand walked up to the front door. On the door was a knocker that was a golden colored lion head. Karl knocked via the door knocker with three solid knocks.

"Will you be staying here too, Karl?" Gramps asked still stunned for the beauty of Copenhagen.

"Oh sadly no, the lady and her daughter who lives here speak English so they will take care of you. They will do all the uh cooking and cleaning and speaking there. I will be your work translator and driver," he said with a half grin.

"Ah okay," Gramps replied with a half grin.

Then, the door opened and there standing in front of them were two ladies. The Mom looked to be in her late 30s or early 40s and the daughter looked to be in her late teens possibly early twenties.

"Well I will let you get acquainted with them," he said and nodded.

As he turns around to head back to the car he turned back to face Gramps.

"Oh yes I almost forgot I have a present from Der Fuhrer in the trunk," he said. He tilted his head back.

Gramps figured his nose was beginning to bleed but didn't ask him as the head tilt is the universal sign of a nose bleed.

After he sucked in hard with his nose Karl opened the trunk and presented Gramps with a Nazi SS uniform with the rank of Captain. It also came with an officer's hat with the metal skull emblem.

"Der Fuhrer thought it would be best if you wore something that would make you blend in. Congratulations Captain," he said with a big smile.

"I don't understand I was only a Lieutenant in the Imperial Service," Gramps surprised, said and visibly in shock.

"Yes, well it seems a promotion must have gone through," he answered with a grin.

"Yes, so it seems. How do I contact you?" Gramps said, still in shock eying the uniform.

Gramps ran his fingers over the uniform and the material felt a bit stiff but smooth. When he ran his fingers over the hat he winced a bit when he came over the metal skull because of it being so cold.

"Ah my telephone number is next to the phone inside," he answered. He cracked his knuckles.

"Ah okay well see you tomorrow, Lieutenant," Gramps said. He glanced back up at him.

He nodded, jumped into the car and left.

Gramps walked back inside the house. As soon as he closed the door he heard something coming down the stairs. He pulled his pistol and spun around on his heels to face the staircase.

"You know Ken I think you just made a new friend," A familiar voice said.

Then all of a sudden Grandpa saw that it was George who was walking down the stairs.

"Goddamn it George! You like die!?" Gramps yelled angrily. He lowered his pistol.

"Well we wouldn't all be here unless we had some sort of death wish don't you think?" George posed. He walked right up to his American partner.

They shook hands and hugged.

"WE??" Gramps asked puzzled. He squinted his eyes.

"Yes, we. Meet Asta and her daughter Hannah." George said and pointed to them.

"Welcome to the Holger Danske Resistance Group." Hannah said in English with a heavy Danish accent.

"Well, this is certainly a surprise. I hope this is not all of the resistance," Gramps remarked. He tried to come up with something clever on the fly.

"No, just one of the safe houses," Asta said in a thick Danish accent with a grin.

"Your English is good both of you," Gramps praised. He shifted his weight from right to left.

"Yes, we uh learn from Father," Hannah answered with a smile.

"Her father was a teacher who taught English. He was killed fightn' the Krauts when they invaded in 1940," George said. He pulled out a stick of gum and popped it in his mouth.

"Oh, I am so sorry," Gramps said with sympathy.

Asta and Hannah nodded.

"Well, I'm beat I'm gonna head to bed," Gramps said lightening the mood.

"Your room is up the stairs and the first door on the left," George said. He chewed and smacked his gum loudly.

"Thanks," Gramps replied and walked up the staircase.

Gramps opened the door to the room and it was quite beautiful. There was a large wooden dresser, closet, a small desk and a large bed. He dropped his duffle at the foot of the bed and belly flopped on to the neatly made bed. He fell fast asleep and awoke sometime later that night. He walked down the stairs and found George awake in the living room with the fireplace blazing. He sat on an armchair and had a glass of Scotch in his hand.

"Come on Ken sit with me," he said. He turned around to face Gramps.

Gramps walked down and sat in the other armchair across from the Englishman.

"Cozy isn't it the fire," he remarked like he was in a trance.

George held the crystal glass and studied it turning the glass ever so slowly, as the light from the fireplace illuminated it.

Gramps watched the flames dance in the fireplace and the crackling of the fire seemed to be the only noise in the entire house.

"Yeah, it certainly is a whole lot different than the jungles of the Philippines. Hell even back home," Gramps replied. He chuckled.

"Drink?" he asked. He held up a bottle.

"No, I'm good did you get to bed yet?" Gramps asked and waved his hand.

"Yeah, I did but I woke up an hour ago and couldn't go back yet," he stated. He cracked his neck.

"Oh, what time is it?" Gramps asked. He massaged the back of his neck.

"3 AM," George answered. He took a sip from his glass.

"Ah, we have a busy day today don't we?" Gramps asked. He looked at him.

"Yeah, we certainly do. Although, I do thank the Heavens that you have the more difficult job," he remarked. He looked at his counterpart.

Gramps laughed.

"Yeah I should get an Oscar for my performance!" Gramps remarked and looked back at the fireplace.

George and Gramps laughed.

"Oh yeah you better ask Winnie 'bout that statue," he remarked. He also set his eyes back on the fireplace.

Gramps chuckled.

"Yeah I'll send him a letter," Gramps answered with a smile.

The pair talked and joked until 6AM three hours later. Around this time Asta and Hannah were waking up and made their way down stairs.

"Oh you both are up already, good," Asta said slightly surprised.

"Yeah just drinkin' scotch at six in the morning," George said. He held up the glass.

"Ah well, how about I brew up some tea, hmm?" Asta asked.

"That would be lovely Asta thanks," Gramps replied with a smile.

Hannah helped her mother whip up breakfast and within 15 minutes they were calling the men to the dining table. Oranges, cups of tea, eggs, ham, and fresh toast made up their breakfast. After breakfast Gramps got dressed and rang up Karl to come and get him.

"Wow Hauptsturmfuhrer huh?" George remarked at Grandpa's uniform.

"Huh what is that?" Gramps asked.

"The rank on your Waffen-SS uniform, its Captain," he said. He pointed to him.

"Oh right Captain yeah you gotta teach me how to say that," Gramps replied.

"Yeah, so when is that driver of yours supposed to arrive?" he asked. He sipped his tea.

"Uh in like 10 minutes," Gramps said. He glanced at his watch.

"Ah so you think you will train German and Danish troops?" he asked. He blew on his tea to cool it off.

"I really don't know, I hope not. I think Krauts will make me a paper pusher where I'll be comfortable," Gramps answered a bit nervous.

"Well nevertheless be ready for anything cause the Jerrys they know how to torture," George said. He looked at Gramps.

"Yeah I hear ya," Gramps remarked. He raised an eyebrow.

Like clockwork Karl arrived at the house 10 minutes later.

"How was your first night in Denmark?" he asked. Gramps got into the car.

"It was nice; I have never had to use a fireplace inside of the house before," Gramps replied. He rubbed his hands together and blew on them for warmth.

Karl laughed.

"Well, get used to it you will have to use one until March when spring comes," he said with a half grin.

"I do enjoy the snow. It's quite something," Gramps remarked. He pulled out a pair of black gloves from his pocket and put them on his icy hands.

Karl laughed and turned around to face him.

"Why is there no snow where you're from?" he asked in surprise.

"No, not in Hawaii. Although we do have black snow every now and then," Gramps replied. He finally began to feel warm.

"Black snow, what is that?" Karl puzzled, asked. He looked back at Gramps again.

"It's uh ash that's released into the air when sugar cane is burning," Gramps said.

"Oh. Do you live on uh Sugar plantation?" he asked intrigued.

"No, I live on a farm," Gramps replied with a smile.

"A farm?" he asked.

"Yes, a dairy farm," Gramps said.

"Ah, I live on a farm too back in Germany," he reveled.

"Really? What kind of farm?" Gramps intrigued, asked and raised an eyebrow.

"My Mother has a garden of fruits and vegetables. The rest of the lands are filled with cattle and horses," he said. He glanced up at Gramps from the car mirror.

"Ah that must have been fun; I have a horse back home," Gramps replied. He pulled out a stick of gum and popped it in his mouth.

Grandpa looked out the window and once again marveled at all that they zoomed by. Brick buildings and Danes mixed with uniformed German soldiers filled the streets. Gas powered cars were only available to the German Army and thus giving birth to quite a few of the first hybrids. There were also many bicycles as well. Present day, Denmark is one of the most bicycle friendly countries in the world.

After reminiscing and trading stories about their homes they arrived at the Nazi Headquarters in Copenhagen. As Karl and walked out of the car they ran into some Enlisted Nazis who gave them the customary Nazi salute. Karl and Gramps returned their salute and yelled out a Heil Hitler (Hail Hitler). After the soldiers left Karl turned to Gramps and spoke.

"You have been practicing?" he asked. He looked at Gramps.

"Well, I figured I should learn that to avoid arousing suspicion," Gramps said. He chewed his gum slowly.

"Good idea," he said with a nod.

The two men walked to the building and the place was crawling with Nazis and they were all armed. Gramps noticed there were a few women all dressed in business attire and he figured they worked in clerical. As he scanned the place with his eyes a Nazi SS Major came over to them and they followed him to his office. Karl and Gramps sat on a par of chairs directly across the Major who sat behind his desk. Once at the office Karl translated on Grandpa's behalf a three way conversation between them. After they shook hands they sat down.

"I am Major Wolf and I have heard many things about you Captain," Karl translated to him.

"Good things, I hope Major," Gramps replied with a smile.

After Karl finished translating Grandpa's response the Major chuckled.

"Yes, quite good things. Drink, cigarette?" he asked in German.

"He said he's heard many good things and he's offering a drink and cigarette," Karl said in English.

"Good thank you uh yes to the first no to the second," Gramps said.

The Major chuckled as Karl translated.

Then, the Major pulled out a bottle of vodka and three glasses from his desk. He then placed them on the top of the desk and began to pour the clear alcohol into the glasses. As Major Wolf handed Karl a cigarette and lit both his and Karl's they began to convers in German. They conversed for a few minutes and had a short laugh. At this point Gramps was feeling like a third wheel on a date with a buddy. As Gramps stared at the bottle he noticed that the label on it was in a symbol like lettering style called Cyrillic and his mind began to race to identify the language. Then, Karl turned to Gramps and filled him in on what the hell was going on.

"I asked the Major about where he had gotten the Vodka and he said it was from a friend. The friend sent him a large wooden crate filled with the stuff with a note that read "recently liberated from the front enjoy!" And he has been enjoying it ever since," Karl said.

"Ah the Eastern Front," Gramps said. He realized what the note meant.

"Yes," Karl replied.

As the Major pulled the cigarette from his lips and puffed a large smoke cloud out from his mouth he held up his glass in a toast and yelled out something in German.

"He said 'To a Thousand Year Reich.' Which basically mean uh without getting into too many details a thousand years of the current German regime," Karl translated.

"Oh, To a Thousand Year Reich!" Gramps yelled. He raised his glass.

"To a thousand Year Reich!" Karl said for Gramps in German.

Karl said it again for himself and raised his glass. They all hit their glasses together in the toast and then they drank their glasses dry. After their glasses were dry the Major spoke and Karl translated simultaneously.

"So, Captain what position do you desire out here in Denmark?" Karl translated as the Major looked at Gramps skeptical.

"Excuse me?" Gramps asked. He looked blankly at the major.

"You were given a posting and a position of your choosing," Karl translated.

"Oh yes silly me now I remember," Gramps covered with a fake smile.

"So, what job do you want to do?" he asked.

"Uh I want to work the office as clerical," Gramps said.

"You? Really? You sure you don't want to train Danish volunteers? Or perhaps be a high guard at a camp?" Karl translated.

"No, in all the killings and tortures that I have seen has made me want to have a change of scenery," Gramps said with a smile.

"Ah you have lost your appetite," Karl translated. He scratched his head.

"Yes, regrettably I have. In the mean time I want to have a relaxing position at least until my appetite returns," Gramps asked. He chewed his gum.

"Ah yes, I know what you mean. And I have a present for you," he said with a grin.

The Major pulled out from his desk a German made Luger P08 pistol with holster and magazines for it. He also pulled out a German made MP-40 submachine gun and magazines for it. He handed them both to Gramps and Karl continued to translate.

"You must have a primary weapon and sidearm with that uniform; it just doesn't seem complete without them," he translated with a smile.

"Thank you," Gramps said in German.

Wolf and Karl began to laugh.

"You can speak German?" Karl asked quite surprised.

"No, I only learned that from Asta so far," Gramps replied with a sly grin.

"Ah that is very good," he commanded. He cleared his throat.

Karl then turned to Wolf and filled him in.

"Well I hope you can learn more, perhaps even become fluent," Karl translated from Wolf.

"Yes," Gramps answered in German with a grin.

Major Wolf said something in German and stood up.

"We are now going to walk over to your office," Karl said.

"My office? I thought you guys didn't know what I was goin' to choose?" Gramps puzzled asked.

"We were prepared for any answer," Karl said. He turned to Gramps and grinned.

"Ah you, I like you folks, you think of everything," Gramps remarked.

They walked over to his office.

They walked two doors down from the Major's and right there he opened the door to Grandpa's office. It was spacious and came equipped with three chairs, a desk, filing cabinet, and assortment paper clips, pens, and other office supplies. Hell, there even was a brand new typewriter on the desk. There was a telephone that also sat on the desk which Gramps figured was monitored by German intelligence, possibly Gestapo or the other agency Abwehr. The three of them did a 'Heil Hitler' and Nazi salute before the Major returned to his office.

"So what are my duties?" Gramps asked.

"Well, you are to just simply file papers in order. You know uh troop movement would be under troops, amounts of petrol or gasoline would be under supplies, and so on. If you do find errors simply correct them and file them. I will be your assistant translating the documents for you until you can speak and read German fluently," he laid out.

"It's a pretty mindless job," Gramps remarked.

"Yes, it is," he said.

"I like it, shall we?" Gramps asked.

"Sure," he replied and they got to work.

All of a sudden all these workers came and dropped files after files on Grandpa's desk. He swore the stacks of papers must have been three feet high at least! Five long hours later it was lunch and Gramps was super relieved. He managed to pull a bunch of documents, fold them and stick it in his pocket while Karl was out of the room. After that they went to lunch and came right back to the office. Some hours later at 5PM they left the office and Karl dropped him back to the house. Gramps walked into the house and immediately gave George the documents he stole from the office.

"Very good Ken. Next time thought you may want to take photographs instead of snatching them up," he said. He studied the documents.

Gramps scoffed.

"Well, perhaps I could if somebody gave me a covert camera," Gramps remarked sarcastically. He looked at George.

George laughed.

"Yeah, I think I have one around," he replied. He got up from the couch. George went upstairs, into his room and emerged back down with a few small cameras. He tossed them to Gramps and then went back to sit down. One of the cameras was so small it could fit in the palm of his hand.

"One roll of film takes about 20 shots and there is a fresh one in there," he said. He sat back down.

"Do we have any more cameras?" Gramps asked. He picked them up and studied them.

"Ah yeah I found a Leica camera and another of those mini cameras," he replied.

Now armed with the camera Gramps was ready for tomorrow. The only thing was how to get Karl out of the room long enough for him to take pictures of the documents? However he still had a bit to think up on that but for now it was dinner and that he was looking forward to. For dinner they had steaks and that was a huge surprise for Gramps. How the ladies managed to obtain such good food all the time was and still is a mystery to

Gramps to this day. He later guessed that it was through the black market or perhaps the Germans themselves keeping their Japanese ally content but he could never confirm it.

Sometime after 10PM a couple members of the Holger Danske resistance group came into the house and they were introduced to them. The two men introduced themselves as Flammen and Citron. Gramps didn't know it at the time but their real names were Bent Faurschou Hviid and Jorgen Haagen Schmith. The two would later become the most well know Danish resistance fighters in Danish history. They talked and said to them that a steady stream of intelligence and supplies was established with George and Gramps. The pair of resistance fighters expressed their concern over British intelligence screwing them but their fears were quickly suppressed when George reveled he and Gramps had a direct line to Churchill.

George conversed with them in Danish and it seemed that they were extremely surprised and delighted about their connection with the British Prime Minister. They seemed by their tone of voice and body language that they were extremely intrigued by the fact that there was no middle man just the duo and Churchill. The advantage of the resistance group was its looseness among its members. Many members didn't know about who else was a member and so even if the Germans had infiltrated it which they did twice they wouldn't know much. The other advantage was that because of looseness it was very certain that Grandpa's and George's identities would be safe even from its members. Plus, the life expectancy of a resistance member was quite short so between George and Gramps there really wasn't much worry about that part.

It would be over some time that Gramps came to understand the Danes and their views on their German occupiers. For now though Gramps was just getting into the role of being a spy in Denmark by day, resistance member and saboteur by night. A few hours later the two resistance members left the house and disappeared into the darkness.

"Well, I'm gonna head to bed," Gramps announced.

"Yeah that sounds good. I think I could use a few extra hours of sleep," George replied.

The partners got up from the couch and went straight to bed. Gramps was planning on tinkering with the camera later that night but he was so tired he forgot to. So the next morning he played around with the camera to see what was what and how he could operate it best and so on. Then, like clockwork Karl picked him up and they went to work.

"You ready to eat?" Karl asked.

"You know what bring me back somethin' I'm gonna stay in and just relax a bit," Gramps said with a smile.

"All right suit yourself," he replied and left.

As soon as the Nazi Lieutenant left for lunch Gramps shut the blinds on the windows and door. He took out the small camera from his pocket and began snapping away document after document. As he snapped away he couldn't help but feel like he was a young boy cheating on a test in school. The excitement and the fried nerves, gave him a rush that he couldn't get enough of. Within ten short minutes he had filled the entire roll of film. He tucked the camera back into his pocket and opened the blinds again. He then sat back down at his desk, threw his head back and rested his eyes. Just as he was going to surrender to sleep the door opened and the aroma of food was suddenly in the air.

"Hey you awake? I brought a plate of food," Karl said. He ushered the plate in and placed it on the desk.

"Hmm thanks Karl," Gramps said. He sat back up and opened his drowsy eyes.

On the plate there was some German sausage and a fresh roll. Gramps wolfed it down at lightning speed. Despite devouring the meal hastily he did get to enjoy it. As his teeth sank into the sausage the casing broke and all the hot juices came rushing into his mouth. The bread was so fresh and steamy.

He broke it apart with his fingers. It was an incredible meal.

"If the meals were always gonna be this good then it would make my job a hell of a lot easier," Gramps thought to himself.

Once Gramps finished eating they worked until it was time to head home. They jumped into the car and Karl dropped him off at the house.

In candid conversations with Major Wolf and Karl, Gramps found out about many atrocities that the pair had committed both in Denmark and on the Eastern Front. What shocked Gramps more than the detailed acts was the fact that they talked about it quite freely like almost bragging and so candid. Major Wolf told Gramps of how he and other had hung villagers from the trees in the forest. In towns they had stuffed all the towns' folk in a church, chained the door and lit it a blaze. They shot all those trying to escape and watched as the screams were music to their ears. They had Jews and others dig their own graves, large pits. Once these mass graves were dug the Germans lined them up and shot them. The two also spoke about hanging parties from any place high; trees, street posts and lamps.

Here in Denmark they spoke very openly about the mass rapes they had committed through this beautiful country since 1940. They smiled and laughed about all of this which only enraged Gramps further. Gramps was trying to conceal his anger but with each story it proved to be counterproductive. They didn't notice the look on Grandpa's face; no they were having too much fun bragging. By the end of the talks he was so pissed off he was shaking uncontrollably. He just wanted to strangle both of the SS officers and the worst part was he knew he could do it in less than five seconds.

"Kyle, time to go," Mom said.

I didn't even hear the screen door open.

"All right see you tomorrow Grandpa," I said I got up from the couch.

I snapped to attention facing him and gave a salute. He stood up from his recline and returned the salute. I grabbed my backpack and walked to the kitchen where mom waited for me. Gramps followed me. He stood by the kitchen table and saw us off. He would do that every time.

"So, what did Grandpa and you talk about this time? Mom asked.

I stared out the window looking at all the houses we passed by. My mind drifted to Copenhagen and everything Grandpa spoke about. Oh, how I wished I could have been there! Even at a young age I didn't see a romance or glory in war but a pride of living through it. After all Gramps was the only person I knew who had been through combat and opened up about it. I wanted to be like him, perhaps too much so. As a kid I have already gone through hardships that most shouldn't and have lots of stories to tell.

After I got home I looked in our encyclopedia set for Denmark and found it. I learned that the country still had a royal family and that the current head is Queen Margrethe II, is the granddaughter of King Christian X. Later that night I laid in bed and thought of all grandpa had told me that day about his adventures in Denmark. It was remarkable how one man can do so much and the fact that I was related to him just made it special. It was then that I decided that I would follow in his footsteps and go to all these countries see what he saw and stand where he stood. I had already longed to go to England so I started to plan a European trip.

Chapter 9

Love and The Crown

Being a spy Grandpa learned that the trick to maintaining a cover was to keep it as close to your real life. For example irreverent things such as your favorite drink or favorite sport could stay the same. However, it was much easier for him because he didn't have to lie or cover up many facts about himself. Sure he had to do some covering up here and there but he really didn't have to create a whole new persona but rather keep switching outlooks. The only problem about sticking too close was to actually believe that your cover is you. This is a great problem mainly for deep cover agents and for those who have been undercover for a long period of time. Gramps thankfully didn't have this problem because of George and other Danish resistance members around. Had he been completely alone with no contacts and no backup he was pretty sure he would have fallen in with the Japanese or the Nazis.

Routine is also key especially when you're undercover because it makes you the least person anyone would expect to be up to something. How Gramps kept himself from going crazy and mixing up things was he had to tell himself lie by day and truthful by night. In essence that is pretty much what he did in Denmark. During this time there were strikes and protests by

Danish civilians all over the country. The Germans didn't seem to mind a bit of protest after all they were not violent, not yet anyway. Had the Germans known about the growing resistance and that the protest was a glimpse of what was to come. He thought things would have been much different.

As the months passed and Gramps became close friends with the Germans as well as some members of the Danish resistance they would go sight-seeing. One day in March Karl and his Danish girlfriend Helga decided to take Gramps on a picnic. They went to Copenhagen Harbor and to Grandpa's surprise they got on a boat and went around the harbor. There were only the three of them on the boat and Karl acted as the skipper. After a beautiful ride that lasted more than two hours they went to see the Little Mermaid statue. The statue was in Langelinie Park and it was a nice stroll for Karl and Gramps who were both avid nature fans. After that they dropped Gramps back at home and went on their way.

"Where the hell did you go?" George asked with an angry look on his face.

"They took me on a boat tour of Copenhagen Harbor," Gramps stated with his cool intact.

"No shit?" George remarked, surprised.

"Yeah and after that we took a walk in Langelinie Park," Gramps said. He took a beer out from the fridge.

"Ah, the Little Mermaid statue," he said. He walked to the couch and sat down.

Gramps nodded and sat down on the couch.

"Yeah I like it," Gramps replied. He popped the bottle open.

"So, did you ask him about a position in the Schalburg Corps HQ?" he asked. He opened up a newspaper.

"Oh shit! I knew I forgot something! Gramps exclaimed and drank.

"Shit, Ken don't blow it," he ordered. He peered above the newspaper.

"Yeah, yeah I know. I'll ask him 'bout it on Monday," Gramps answered. He took another chug of his beer.

"Oh and we're havin' Flammen and Citron over again later tonight," George said.

"Ah weapons demo?" Gramps asked.

He nodded. He folded the paper in half to get a better look at a story.

"Yep I got a fresh batch of arms from London," he said.

At 11PM under the cover of darkness the two resistance fighters arrived at the house. Once inside George led them into the basement where he kept the weapons. Once down there they opened up a bottle of Scotch and relaxed. George then showed them eight handguns and a British Sten submachine gun. The resistance fighters went by the codenames of Falmmen and Citron. At some point during the showing Flammen picked up the Sten and pulled the trigger. George had pulled out all the rounds of all the guns but the Sten and he now had three rounds implanted in his left ass cheek. They were all drunk and laughing about it as they plucked out the rounds with a knife. The three of them managed to stitch George up good and returned to the weapons demonstration which turned into a massive drinking contest.

At nights George with his SOE training had taught Gramps how to create homemade napalm, claymores and bombs that would be later called improvised explosive devices or IEDs. He had seen a bit of how the Japanese had rigged things up but because they had just won control of the Philippines they didn't set too many of these. It was rather looting, breaking POWs and controlling their slave laborers that was concern.

Flammen and Citron drank Gramps under the table so much so that when he attempted to stand up he fell face first onto the cement floor. After that they staggered back up the steps and George and Gramps bid them a drunken goodbye at 3AM. Then, the two of them crawled their way up the steps to their rooms and Gramps passed out as he flopped on the bed. The next day Gramps awoke at 2PM to the worst hangover he ever had. Everything seemed to be amplified by a hundred fold. Lights, sounds and his head felt like it was going to explode. He put on a pair of dark black sunglasses and walked down to the kitchen.

"Well, good afternoon," Hannah said. She tried not to laugh.

"What? Oh yeah thanks," Gramps mumbled.

"What K hungover?" George asked. He got up from the couch.

"Oh go to hell George!" Gramps replied and gave him the middle finger.

George laughed.

"How's the ass?" Gramps asked with a laugh.

"Oh fuck off!" He replied with the middle finger in the air.

Gramps laughed.

Hannah made Gramps a sandwich which by some miracle he managed to hold down. The rest of the day was a lazy day and Gramps drank as much water as possible. He wanted to get over the hangover as fast as he could. It's a big surprising that he didn't throw up even once but he still was miserable as shit! As he laid on the couch George was still haggling him about being hungover. The Englishman sat on a chair and was reading Dracula by Bram Stoker. Gramps fell asleep and woke up just in time for dinner. After dinner Gramps had language lessons from Hannah and George. When Gramps decided to turn in at 10PM George, Asta and Hannah were talking about sabotaging a railway or something like that.

The next day after Karl picked Gramps up and they went to the office. Once they got settled in the office Gramps talked to him about the Schalburg Corps Headquarters' job. The Schalburg Corps was Danish volunteers who joined up with the Nazi SS. So, in other words it was the headquarters for the Danish SS. With all the language practice Gramps was able to carry on a short conversation in both Danish and German. So, he decided to chat with Karl in German about the position. To improve his skills he would first begin in Danish or German and then when he couldn't understand anymore he would switch back to English.

"Hey so what about that position with Schalburg HQ?" Gramps asked in German.

"It's still open, why?" he replied in German. He peered at him.

"I want it," Gramps answered.

"Working at Danish SS Headquarters why would you want that?" he asked taken back.

"Cause I wanna see how it is," Gramps replied in English.

"You German is getting good," he said in English.

"Thanks. Besides I heard they have beautiful women working there," Gramps remarked with a sly grin.

"Oh really? We shall go there at once and find you a girl," Karl played along.

Gramps started to laugh and Karl joined in.

"I will inform Major Wolf of their request for transfer for office work at Schalburg HQ," Karl stated.

Gramps nodded and they got onto the work of the day.

Three days later the request was approved and a week later Gramps and Karl were working at the Danish SS headquarters. It went smoothly until August 28 that was the day the Nazis gave the Danish Government a choice; get your people under control or we will. Public protest and strikes were widespread and more often than before. This was also around the time that the amount of sabotage revved up and reached the breaking point with the Germans. The Danish Government refused to and so the next day to prevent the Germans from having all the ships of the Danish Navy the government ordered their sailors to sabotage or scuttle the ships. Some of the ships made their way with success to neutral Sweden right next door. The Germans managed to capture a few ships before the Danes could damage it. For the most part the Danes succeeded in making sure the Germans didn't get their hands on the most of the ships. The Government Co-op between the Danes and the Germans was over and the Danish government dissolved.

Just days prior to the co-op falling apart Gramps had taken Mindy, a 27 year old women on a date and then well they got to know each other 'intimately.' Mindy was a friend of Karl's girlfriend and like any good friends would do they played matchmaker on them. After dinner Mindy and him went back to her place where they made hot love. She pushed him onto the bed and seductively undressed. Well, I'm sure you can envision what happened next. Mindy had a skinny body and stood at a short five-foot-three. She had these dark blue eyes that looked like the waters of the Pacific and had long natural platinum blond hair. She streak white smile and a tender voice.

The next night Gramps heard George playing a melody on a Violin and it was so sweet and unlike anything he had ever heard. Gramps was quite taken back by it and so he pulled his harmonica and joined it. The song was Pachelbel's Canon by Johanna Pachelbel (1653-1706), a German composer of classical music. This one song kicked off his love affair with classical music and Violins that would last the rest of his life. George stopped playing and handed Gramps the violin to examine it.

"Beautiful isn't it? It's a Stradivarius crafted in 1721," George said.

Gramps laid transfixed by the instrument.

The violin was a dark shade of brown in color. Gramps glided his fingers on the back of the violin's smooth back. The back of the wood was smooth like glass. He also ran his fingers around the instrument's half-moon shaped hooks along both sides of the body.

Then as if the moment couldn't get any better it did, George pulled out an identical looking 1721 Stradivarius for Gramps. Under the Englishman's guidance Gramps began to learn how to play it. As Gramps mastered playing the stunning instrument George gave him the pair shortly before they departed Denmark. Gramps still has the pair of violins somewhere and it still does sound as beautiful as the first time he heard it play.

Also during the summer 1943 Hannah took Gramps to Tivoli gardens amusement park. The park was immensely crowded and there were lots of children all over the place. George was around too but he kept his distance as a precaution in case they were being watched. In any case he was right the Gestapo or the German Secret Police was in fact monitoring Gramps.

They didn't make the connection with George and Gramps but they concluded that he was going out with two women. It didn't bother the Gestapo of his womanizing character but they made a note that it might be useful later. They were watching Gramps because he had peaked their curiosity as well as their suspicions. He was after all not a not a European nor was he an Imperial Japanese Army solider. No, he was an American who had turned, became an Imperial solider and because of Germany's alliance with Japan, now wore the uniform of a Waffen-SS Captain in occupied Denmark.

The Gestapo agents walked in plain clothes around the park while he was having a blast with Hannah. They rode all the rides and enjoyed the food as well. When Hannah and Gramps rode the rollercoaster it didn't feel like there was a war raging and that he was in an occupied country. It was in that moment that he had forgotten about the war, being a spy, everything. He felt like he was out with a close friend and it was just an ordinary day. However, the moment was short lived and as the ride finished the reality of the fact that he was a spy in the middle of an occupied country during a war sunk in once more. What goes up must come down, right? He didn't really recall when it happened but sometime during this fun filled day he and Hannah began to hold hands. They didn't kiss until later that evening. After they had spent nearly the entire day there they decided to head home. Before that Gramps excused himself and went to the bathroom. George followed him and they checked all the stalls to make sure they were alone and then they began to talk.

"I met a girl and will being goin' home with her," George said with this big goofy grin all over his mug.

Gramps laughed.

"All right have fun," Gramps replied.

"Ohh always," he replied with a sly smile.

"Will you be back for dinner?" Gramps asked. He looked at the door.

"Uh I think so. I have to message Winnie regarding supplies to the Danish resistance," he said. He scratched his nose

"Oh yeah they have been complaining about for some time," Gramps remarked.

"Yeah, so I'll be home around 10," George said.

Gramps nodded.

"Well, watch for Krauts," Gramps remarked.

George laughed.

"Yeah, likewise. You carryin' ?" he asked.

"Always. You?" Gramps replied and tapped his lower back.

"Yep," he answered and tapped his chest.

The partners nodded and Gramps walked out first. When Hannah and Gramps were out of sight after a few minutes George emerged from the bathroom and walked away. Thankfully the Gestapo had not made the connection and they never would.

The cars that civilians had were not powered by oil but by a wood burning one. They had this type of furnace like generators that powered it. Oil vehicles were reserved for the German military. Since the different vehicles most civilians and resistance members could tell if a German was coming from a mile away.

Once Gramps and Hannah got home they discovered a note on the kitchen table from Asta stating that she was out doing errands. The couple had the entire house to ourselves and they made the best of it.

"Do you like me?" Hannah said softly.

"Yes, I do," Gramps softly replied as he gazed deep into her blue ocean like eyes.

"Grandpa!" I groaned in disgust.

"What! We were both teenagers. People like us, just kids fightin' and dyin' it was nice to do somethin' normal," Grandpa explained.

I nodded in agreement.

When Asta her mom came home they acted as if nothing had happened but a relaxed day at Tivoli Gardens. Hell, they even managed to keep their relationship a secret from George until mid-October.

To maintain his cover and now another secret Grandpa saw Mindy until mid-October and then he hooked up with Elsa a twenty something year old bartender. By this time he was quite fluent in Danish and German. He could speak it but his reading still needed some work. One night Hannah came into his room and they had well you can use your imagination. He guessed they must have been a bit too loud because George awoke and heard them going at it. The Englishman confronted Gramps later the next day alone and he agreed to keep the relationship secret from Asta.

Gramps enjoyed his time in Denmark so far. He watched the leaves turn with the changing of the seasons. The people and nature of this beautiful country was unparalleled and made such a mark on him that even after all these years he never forgot it. Some nights really late he would go outside and glance at the sky to see the stars. Some night it would be cloudy while others would be so clear you could see each individual star illuminate and twinkle in the darkness of the night. He taught George and Hannah all the constellations that he saw. They laughed and had a ball doing so even if it was freezing outside.

After the fall of the Danish Government resistance operations revved up and many acts became more gutsy and public. Shooting in the middle of the day, increase of strikes that became violent, bombing Pro-Nazi and Nazi buildings and they even went as far as disarming German soldiers at gunpoint in broad daylight. Many Danish cops were also for the resistance and informed them on if there was going to be a raid or if the Germans were gonna arrest someone. Even, George was getting to kill Germans or Danish civilians working for them. Gramps wanted to get into the action but to maintain his cover he couldn't and that really made his blood boil.

"I'm in a Nazi occupied country I wanna kill some Nazis!" Gramps eagerly exclaimed.

"Yeah I know you do Ken but you gotta keep you cover," George stressed. He fixed himself a drink.

"Well shit! Message Winnie that I wanna kill Nazis," Gramps grumbled. "Got it. Oh and uh you and I have been requested to meet King Christian X," he said. He took a sip of the Johnny Walker Blue in his glass.

"What? When? How?" Gramps asked in surprise.

"He wants to meet the two of us in secret of course at the palace in December. More details to follow as we get closer," he explained like it was nothing.

"Ah so just playin' it by ear," Gramps remarked. He rubbed his eyes.

"Yes, in any case we should see if our suits still fit as we have been eating rather well here," he said. He tapped his stomach.

"Yeah, good idea," Gramps said. He glanced down at his own stomach.

One day in November when Karl was out at home hurling his guts out from the Flu, three Gestapo agents paid Gramps a visit in his office. They rounded him up at gunpoint with a luger, forced him to walk with them to their car and then they took a drive to their headquarters. They then led him to a dim lit room with a wooden table in the center, tied his wrists to a chair and proceeded to interrogate him.

"Who do you work for?" One of the Gestapo men yelled in German.

"Your mother!" Gramps shot back in German with a grin.

The Gestapo agent punched him in the jaw. He went back and to the side. It was a solid hit. He was a bit dazed from the combo of whacking the wall behind him.

"Ohh you boys will be a lot of trouble when your boss finds out!" Gramps remarked. He spat out blood at them.

They laughed.

"Yeah? Not after we kill you!" One spat.

Who are you working for? The Americans? The British? The Canadians?" another yelled angrily in German and got in his face.

Just as one of them was going to strike him with his fist, Gramps told them.

"Wait! I'll tell!" He screamed.

"WHO! TELL US!" they screamed in German.

"Your old lady! Your old lady! And your old lady! Gramps yelled. He looked to each of the three Gestapo men.

Gramps laughed hard as a Gestapo hit him in the gut quite hard. He crumpled to the ground in agony and still continued to laugh. The fall was just enough time to slip his right hand out of the ropes. He had broken his hand while riding a bicycle when he was nine and never went to the doctor. So, the wrist healed but similar to dislocating a shoulder he was able to pop his wrist out. He spat blood on them and got back up, still laughing. By the time the three agents knew he was free it was too late. Gramps swung the chair into the face of one and it large pieces of wood rained as the chair shattered. The man dropped to the ground after the solid it.

'Two left,' Gramps thought. He flashed a crazed grin.

The other two agents now suddenly terrified backed into two corner of the room. Gramps undid the ropes of his left wrist and tossed the armrest to the side. The second man swung his fist towards his face. Grandpa swatted it away with a block. He kicked his enemy in the groin. The man bent over and howled in pain. Gramps then with all his might used a roundhouse kick to his head. The second man when down cold on the floor. The third man was not so interested into going like his partners. He grabbed a Karabiner 98 Kurtz or Kar98 rifle hidden under the wooden table. The bayonet on the rifle sparkled as the light hit it. The gestapo agent thrusted the rifle at him. Gramps, side stepped, grabbed the rifle, unhooked the bayonet and sliced his enemy's hand with it. The third agent screamed in pain and let go the rifle. Grandpa dropped the bayonet on the table and swung the rifle butt to the man's face. He went down to the floor with a loud thud.

Grandpa stuck the bayonet back onto the rifle, pulled the bolt back to chambered a round and opened the door. There right in front him a crowd of ten Gestapo agents with a mixture of Luger P08 pistols and MP40 submachine guns, cocked and aimed directly at him. Before he could react two other agents he didn't see gave him the butts of their weapons to the right and left of his head. It was now his turn to unconsciously hit the floor.

This story of Grandpa getting the shit beaten out of him is much like how I felt after he died. It's called depression. I was 16 when he passed and anyone knows that just being that age is hard enough but to have your best friend who you took care of die well that's a hard place to get back from. In that vortex of darkness which lasted years I found relief in acts that would give me relief while further descending into the darkness until there was not a single speck of light. I would see a trailer of a new movie coming out soon or read an article about something, my immediate though would be tell Gramps all about it. I would pick up the phone and two digits from a complete number, my mind would take me back to the sight of his lifeless body in the bed. I would then be frozen in pain and completely unaware of the phone in my hand until that loud beeping tone would sound. No matter what I did it's like the light died with him. I was alone, in the darkness and everything reminded me of him. With my depression I felt like him in that room getting the shit beaten out of him.

When Grandpa woke up he found himself in another room on another chair with one hell of a headache. He was not bound nor restrained in any way. Just then the door opened. In front of him stood Major Wolf.

"Ah good you are awake. You have a phone call waiting," Major Wolf said.

He poured Gramps a drink and handed him the glass. Gramps in turn grabbed the bottle and began to chug it down like a kid's first week in college.

"Who is it?" Gramps groaned and set the bottle down.

Wolf handed Gramps a towel and he wiped the blood off his face.

"It's better if you find out for yourself," he replied coyly.

Gramps got up from the chair and walked with the Major. He led the way. He led Gramps down a hallway and into an office. There in the office a Gestapo Major was on the phone and as soon as they walked in he handed it off to Gramps and they hastily cleared the room.

"Hello?" Gramps answered in German.

"Are you hurt, captain?" A male voice on the other end asked in German.

"Nothing I can't recover from, sir," Gramps remarked as his eyebrow shot up still unsure of the voice on the other end.

"Good to hear, captain," the voice replied.

"May I ask who are you, sir?" Gramps asked, intrigued. He sat down in a chair and got comfortable.

"I am Der Fuhrer," the voice said.

"Oh I am sorry I didn't recognize your voice Mr. Hitler. It is a bit different than the one I hear on the newsreels." Gramps replied, quite surprised.

Hitler chuckled.

"Yes well it is all right. I want you to know that we greatly value our Japanese Allies and know that the men who beat you will be punished with no mercy," Hitler said.

"Thank you very much, *mein Fuhere*," Gramps replied, still stunned.

"So, how has your posting gone in Denmark so far?" he asked.

"It has been good. I have learned to speak German and Danish fluently. And I can read a bit but it still needs work," Gramps said.

"Marvelous! You have adapted much better and have learned much more than I expected," he praised.

"Thank you sir. I have greatly enjoyed my time in Denmark and look forward to spending much more here," Gramps stated.

"Yes, well if you ever have any problems do not hesitate to call me," he said.

"Thank you *mein Fuhrer*," Gramps graciously replied and they hung up.

After Gramps put the handset back on the cradle he walked out of the office and asked Major Wolf if he knew where the Gestapo agents that brought him in were.

"Hitler recalled them to Berlin," Major Wolf said. He pulled out a cigar and some matches from his pocket.

"Wow," Gramps speechless replied.

"Yes, it seems that you have a great and high friend," he remarked. He studied Gramps with his eyes and lit his cigar that dangled from his lips.

"So it seems," Gramps replied.

"Come on I'll take you home," he said.

Gramps nodded and they were off.

It was later that Gramps heard the true fate of three Gestapo men. They met their demise by being forcefully pushed out of airplane mid-flight. They fell to their deaths from several thousand feet somewhere over Europe. Upon discovering how they met their demise he would not lie, he was very happy at it. They were very bad and evil men who deserved it and much more. As he thought back now, he realized that he rubbed shoulders with some of the evilest people to have ever been born. However, on a lighter note he also got to know quite well some of the greatest souls of the 20th Century.

For the entire car ride to Grandpa's house they didn't even speak a single word. Wolf was not a very talkative person unless it involved booze or women or both. Gramps didn't mind the silence at the time because his brain raced through the fact that he had just had a one on one phone conversation with Adolf Hitler. Did that just really happen? He pondered away in silence. When they arrived at the house, Gramps got out of the car and thanked Wolf for driving him home. The Major nodded and smiled. Gramps closed the car door and then Wolf drove off. When Gramps got into the house George was sitting on the dining table eating a snack of toast and jam.

"You're early," George remarked. He slid some jam over a piece toast with a metal knife.

"Yes, and you won't believe why," Gramps swiftly replied.

After Gramps had told George the entire story of him being dragged away, interrogated by Gestapo agents and the phone conversation with Hitler, he just sat there in shock with his mouth open and the toast in his hand, it looked like he was frozen there.

"George you all right? You look like you're havin' a fuckin' stroke or some shit," Gramps remarked and took the jam-laden toast from the Englishman's hand.

"Yeah no I'm fine just processing," he replied with his facial features still frozen in shock.

"It's a lot, ain't it?" Gramps remarked. He bit into his crunchy toast.

"Yes, it certainly is Ken," he blinked a few times and was back to his old self.

"Mmm! This is really good!" Gramps exclaimed, with his mouth full.

"Well, I'm glad you like *my* toast," George shot a peeved look at his partner.

"My complements to ya!" Gramps replied with a smug look on his mug. He took another bite.

"Yeah, yeah," George muttered.

The duo began to bust with laughter, and George tried to pull a large piece of the toast from Grandpa's mouth. Gramps bit on it hard and the crispy toast broke into two pieces. They laughed, and George popped the piece of toast in his mouth and chewed with a large smile.

One month later Gramps was woken up from his sleep by George, who told him to get dressed and ready because the duo was going to meet the king.

"When do we meet the old man?" Gramps groggy asked.

"Uh half an hour," George glanced at his watch.

Gramps nodded, and George left the room so he could get dressed.

Gramps changed into a suit with a blue shirt, striped blue tie, black dress shoes, black pants and a black coat. He rubbed his eyes and yawned. He hid a pistol in the coat pocket and strapped a commando dagger to his ankle. After that, he sailed down the stairs where George waited patiently on the couch near the fireplace.

"Should we take my car?" Gramps asked.

"Yeah that would be good," George replied with a nod.

George grabbed the keys from the dining table, and they went outside. They hopped in the car, and George drove to the palace.

Since the co-op dissolved the streets were wild with protesters and clashes with German soldiers as well as Danish Nazis were common. The SS and the Danish Nazis were the main ones nailing the protests and trying to enforce the curfew but it wasn't working. So, it would be less likely to get stopped by the Germans or the Danish Nazis if they were driving in a regular car as opposed to a civilian one. Gramps just hoped they wouldn't be stopped for any reason. The other worry that he had was that they would be the victim of an attack by the Danish resistance, since only five members really knew who Gramps was. However, they got to the palace with no problems. Because the meeting was ultra-secret, George had received instructions on when and where they were going to meet. As they walked into the palace, Gramps marveled at the walls and the objects inside. Security must not have been doing rounds in the area because they didn't run into a single person while walking around.

George and Gramps walked up some steps, into a hallway and they knocked on the door.

"Enter," A male voice said in Danish.

George opened the door and closed it behind them. A giant man dressed in a black suit greeted them. He was perhaps over a foot taller than Gramps so six foot six.

"I am Christian X, King of Denmark," he introduced himself modestly.

"Major George, Special Operations Executive, Great Britain," George said in Danish. He bowed.

"Captain Kinjiro Kabazawa, SOE, United States of America," Gramps saluted.

King Christian X who stood at a giant six foot seven bowed to George and returned Grandpa's salute. He went back to his chair, sat down and motioned the duo to sit on the two other chairs across of him. The room looked like the office with a nice desk between the SOE Agents and the King.

"You are American? Are they involved with Denmark too?" King Christian X asked, a bit surprised.

"Yes and no, Sir. I'm uh on loan to Prime Minister Churchill," Gramps replied. he scratched his cheek.

"Ah I see so how did you wind up in the service of the British?" he posed.

"Well, that is a long story but the short version is because of you, sir." Gramps replied. He cracked his neck.

"Me?" he asked, surprised.

"Yes, you asked Churchill for help and he sent us," Gramps explained. He scratched his head nervously.

The King shifted his weight around and got comfortable in his seat again. "Oh yes the Prime Minister doesn't disappoint," King Christian remarked with a smile.

"No, he doesn't," George said with a grin.

"Oh where are my manners, you men want a drink?" he asked and stretched out his hand.

George and Gramps quickly glanced at each other and nodded.

"Yes, we would love that, sir," Gramps replied. He turned back to face the King.

"Fantastic," the King responded.

The King then pulled out from behind the desk a beautiful glass bottle and three glasses. He set the glasses on the desk, took the top off of the bottle and poured the brown stuff evenly in each glass. When he finished the glass he put the top back on the bottle and set it on the desk as well.

"May I, sir?" Gramps asked with great respect.

"Please and call me Christian I believe you men have earned that right," he said very casually.

"Thank you Christian," Gramps replied. He took a glass from the table and held it in his hand.

George took a glass as well and Christian did too.

"What shall we toast to gentlemen?" Christian asked, full glass in hand.

"To a free Denmark," Gramps said. He held his glass up.

"To a free Denmark," George seconded with a smile. he held his glass next to Grandpa's.

"To a free Denmark," Christian said with a chuckle. He hit their glasses together in a toast.

Their glasses clinked softly as they hit each other's glass and then they drank. After the first gulp they set their glasses back on the desk and began talking once more.

"So, George are the British going to send more guys like you and Kinjiro?" he asked.

"Like us? None. Although I'm sure that SOE, MI5, MI6 have men here. And they will be sending many more for sure," George said. He scratched his nose.

"Ah yes so, what do you men do on free time at home?" Christian asked.

"Home? Oh uh hiking, swimming, fishing, riding on horseback," Gramps answered without skipping a beat though he had nearly all but forgotten what home liked like anymore.

Christian's face lit up after Gramps mentioned horses and for good reason he was an avid equestrian or horse rider.

"What kind of horse do you have?" Christian asked, intrigued.

"A white one named Shirley," Gramps replied. He took a sip from his glass.

"Ah beautiful creatures horses are they not?" he said with a smile.

"Yes, they certainly are something else," Gramps said with a smile.

Christian who was loosening up still looked and talked like he was very uptight. Gramps supposed that because of the times he had perhaps forgotten to relax or maybe he just didn't want to look vulnerable and as desperate for help. He was. Whatever the reason he was a great King to the people of Denmark and a good man.

"I don't have horses at home but I do have a pair of dogs," George said. He massaged the back of his neck.

"Really? What kind?" Christian asked, intrigued.

"Two Golden Retrievers," he answered. He took a sip from his glass.

"Those are beautiful as well," Christian said. He scratched his head.

"Indeed," Gramps remarked.

"Thanks and yes I agree," George said. He got out a handkerchief and blew his nose with it.

The men chatted for three hours about their personal lives and it was a surprisingly candid moments for George and Gramps considering they were conversing with an old school monarch. They talked fishing, sports, food, and everything under the sun. Gramps came to like the King even though this was the first and last time he would ever meet him.

"You know I envy you men," Christian said out of the blue.

"Why is that you are a King!" Gramps replied, quite taken back.

He nodded.

"Because I am a King I cannot personally strike back at my enemies," he explained.

George and Gramps nodded in understanding. Both he and George had gotten their chance to strike back at their enemies. England was bombed by the Germans and George got to kill some in the field. Kauai and Oahu was bombed by the Japanese and Gramps got his chance to kill Japanese troops in the field. Christian because of the fact that he was the king he couldn't do what the ordinary Dane or agent like the men could. No, all he could do was support the resistance and all efforts against the Germans from the sidelines. He really wanted more than anything was to stand on the frontline with his fellow Danes and take back his country from the Germans. It killed him knowing that the duo had their revenge and he would never have his.

Christian took to a liking to Gramps faster and much more that he did George because he knew what it was like to be a prisoner in his own country like the Monarch. Although, Gramps wasn't in the U.S. for very long after the attack on Pearl Harbor he went through first hand some of the repercussions immediately after. Probably as a result of this bond Gramps had Christian offered him a high-ranking position in the Danish government after the war was over. Besides a cushy job that paid well he also offered Gramps vast lands and a nice title.

"Thank you very much for the incredible offer. I am greatly honored by it and will give it much consideration," Gramps floored answered.

Christian nodded.

Shortly after that they got up to leave and they exchanged handshakes with Christian. Then like how the duo came they left covertly under the cover of darkness. When they got home and the Englishman turned off the car engine George and Gramps just sat there as the experience of chatting with the King of Denmark fully sank in.

"Did that just-

"Yeah it did," Gramps replied and finished George's sentence.

The men then both looked at each other and began to laugh. The idea that they lowly commoners had just spent three and a half hours plainly talking with a six foot seven 73-year-old King was just completely insane but it did happen. Gramps would come to realize later that many of the things that happened in his life were completely insane but he would brush them off as normal.

Chapter 10

A Danish Christmas

When Gramps and George finally got out of the car, into the house and ready for bed, they pulled out their violins and played a bit. If you could picture the scene with the room only lit by fire, the sweet sounds of a pair of violins playing combined with the soft cracklings of the fire. If Gramps closed eyes now he could still hear that music, smell that wood burning and feel the slight chill of a Danish winter.

Gramps believe they woke Asta and Hannah up but they didn't seem to mind because they pulled an acoustic guitar and a cello. Hannah sat on the armchair and began to join in with them playing. This is perhaps one of his favorite memories of his life. Everyone was happy and for once everything was perfect if only for that one moment. After the song ended George jumped on to the piano and they played a piece by Ludwig Van Beethoven called Moonlight Sonata. After that they played two more songs one by Wolfgang Amadeus Mozart and the last by Johann Sebastian Bach. Once the classical show was over they all laughed and clapped before saying good night and finally heading to bed for good.

I remember a story from Gramps during the first Christmas after he passed. The bone cold chill and scent of the Christmas tree, a Norfolk pine brought the memory back. He told it to me on a sleepless night just like this one. He and Grandma spent Christmas Eve at our house that year. I got out of bed after I lost the battle to sleep and was wide awake. I remember him sitting at the end of the big couch lit just by the strings of multi colored lights on the Christmas tree. A steady stream of steam danced out of a ceramic coffee mug on the table.

"You no can sleep too?" he said. He sipped his mug.

"No," I said I shook my head.

He laughed softly and patted the couch cushion next to him. I walked to the couch and sat down next to him. I winced as the coldness of the microfiber touched my bare skin.

Gramps made not a sound he just stared straight at our white wall. His face showed no emotion, not sadness nor anguish, just complete bank, nothing. It was his eyes that gave him away. He had this stare I knew all too well, memories of winter's past and folks from long ago were on his mind.

Later in the day when they had woken up from their slumber Hannah got on the piano and proceeded to break into ragtime music. It was fantastic, they all started to dance and it was just a great time. These are some moments that he would forever remember and cherish. On Christmas Eve 1943 George received two letters from home.

"Oh fuck me!" George exclaimed. He read the letters.

"What is it?" Gramps asked.

"Well, my father suffered a stroke and died. My mother is in the hospital recovering from a heart attack and my girlfriend left me for my best friend," George said. He held the letters.

"Holy shit! I think you broke a couple of mirrors or some shit cause damn brah!" Gramps exclaimed.

"Yeah no fuck! You got anything from your family?" he replied. He folded the letters back up.

"No, they don't even know where I am," Gramps said with a sigh. George nodded.

"The life of a covert agent," he remarked with sympathy. Gramps nodded and sighed.

"Yeah, sorry 'bout everything back home," Gramps replied. He put his hand on the Englishman's shoulder.

"Yeah well shit happens," he remarked with a grin.

"You wanna get tanked?" Gramps asked. He held up a bottle. George laughed.

"Hell yeah. I'll get the glasses," George said.

The two of them ended up drinking the entire bottle in a span of a couple of hours. Needless to say, they were pretty happy after that. After they drank that bottle dry they got together with Asta and Hannah and opened presents.

If you have ever opened presents really drunk it's a ball because you see two or three of that one present. So, you try to open the other two and they end up being just air that you're waving at. Gramps had gotten Asta and Hannah a couple bottles of perfume and a beautiful black leather handbag. George had gotten Gramps and himself bottles of champagne which the Englishman mostly drank. They also had a nice spread of food with steaks and sausages as well as desserts that would make your teeth rot just by thinking about them.

When they had finished eating they went outside and played in the snow. They did snowball wars and snow angels. Especially around the holidays Gramps thought of his family and how everyone was doing. Were they in good heath or ill? Were they financially okay? Did they miss him as much as he did them? Home seemed so far away from here and he feared that they would not recognize him when he got back, whenever that would be. The German were starting to lose the war but the question remained was when and how would it all end?

As Gramps rang in the New Year 1944, he felt this blanket of guilt of not being able to tell his parents about how he was doing just swarm itself over him. So, without thinking he got a pen and some paper and began to write it all down. He wrote every detail of everything that had happened since he had left Waimea which seemed like lifetimes ago. Then, his concentration was broken by the sound of someone knocking on his open door. He turned around to see who it was and George with a blank expression on his face stood there with a paper in his hand.

"What is it?" Gramps concerned asked.

"Winnie is pulling us out of Copenhagen," George said. His face still blank in shock.

"Oh are we heading to somewhere like Odense?" Gramps asked.

"No, he's pulling us out of Denmark," he said with a mortified look on his face.

"What?! No, no! I wanna stay here!" Gramps exclaimed with a combination of shock and anger on his mug.

"I know. All the message said was that we would be pulled out of Denmark on the 8th of January," he said still mortified.

"Does it say where we are headin' next?" Gramps asked, still in shock.

"Yeah London," George replied. He folded up the piece of paper and placed it in his pocket.

"You think you'll be able to drop in on your folks?" Gramps asked. He massaged the back of his sore neck.

"Too soon to say cause I don't know how long I'll be in town for," he answered.

Gramps nodded.

"Yeah well Happy New Year," Gramps said.

"Happy New Year Ken," George replied.

Aerial fireworks blew up in their lighting the sky in shades of blue, red, orange, yellow, purple and pink.

"1944, I wonder if this will be the year the war ends?" Gramps thought in his head.

Of course history would show that the war doesn't end in 1944 but it is the beginning of the end. When the Allies successfully pulled of Operation Overlord which would become known as the Invasion of Normandy in France on June 6, 1944 it looked as if the end was to be by Christmas. However, many more people would die before it would be all over and the Nazis would show their teeth. In the Pacific the U.S. was island hopping their way around battling the Japanese. The war in the Pacific was just as if not more bloody and ferocious than the one that raged in Europe. Like Europe, the Pacific would be won but it would be a bloody and costly road to victory. A new and devastating weapon would be used against the Japanese not once but twice before they would quit. But Gramps was getting ahead of himself as most of this didn't happen yet.

The next night George and Gramps broke the news to Asta and Hannah about their departure. The women pleaded with them to either stay or take them to London too.

"Can we take them with us?" Gramps asked concerned. He turned to George.

"I don't know. Getting letters to England is one thing but smuggling two people out is another entirely different matter," George replied.

"Yeah, I know but can we get them out?" Gramps asked concerned.

"Even if we do I don't know if we would ever see them again," he answered with a sigh.

Gramps turned and looked at Asta and Hannah, then back a George.

"I don't care what anyone says fuck it all they are coming to London with us," Gramps stated defiant.

"You what? Fuck em we're takin' them with us," he said. He fed off Grandpa's defiance.

Asta and Hannah squealed in delight and gave both George and Gramps a great big hug.

"Thank you both so much!" Asta and Hannah said with glee.

"Always," Gramps softy replied.

"Are you crying, George?" Gramps asked. He looked at him.

"No, just got somethin' stuck in my eye that's all," he replied. He wiped his eyes with his hands.

"Yeah, so do I," Gramps replied. Hannah wiped the tears from his eyes.

As members of the resistance if they were uncovered or suspected by the Germans Asta and Hannah would be tortured and killed.

All four resistance members were a great big mess and once they were able to stop the flow of tears George made the moment lively.

"I think this calls for a drink, anybody wanna join me?" he asked. He lightened the mood.

"George you are always thirsty," Asta remarked. A grin began to form on her face.

George rummaged in the kitchen and pulled out a chilled bottle of champagne.

"Well, sure you know there a war going on. You never know when it will be your last drink. So, live it up I say," he half-jokingly replied. He brought the bottle and glasses.

They laughed a bit.

He popped the cork out and poured the good stuff into their glasses and handed it to them.

"Cheers!" Gramps said. They clinked their glasses and George with the champagne bottle.

They took a sip from their glasses while George gulped it down directly from the bottle.

"You- you drink directly from the bottle you contaminate us with germs!" Asta yelled and slapped him.

"Well, none of us are dead yet so, why the hell not!" George replied with a goofy grin.

They all began to burst out in laughter.

After it was all over and the girls had gone to bed George and Gramps sat out in the living room and he confided in Gramps that he didn't know if because of their new additions the entire group would be caught and everything would come out right there and then.

"They are worth the risk," Gramps replied. He looked at the Englishman with a serious look.

"All right I'm just letting you know if we do this none of us may get out alive," George replied.

"I know. You gonna message Winnie 'bout our two new additions?" Gramps asked with a grin.

"It would be ideal to however I believe we can manage," he stated.

"All right well just keep me posted regarding our escape," Gramps said. He nodded.

"Good night," he said.

"Good night," Gramps repeated.

Gramps walked up the stairs and dove in the sheets of his soft bed. He was in the bed just a few minutes before Asta knocked on his open door and walked into the room. She sat right next to him on the bed. He sat up and then found out what was on her mind.

"I know you care for my daughter and so I believe you should know something. That German who used to drive you around Karl, was the one who killed my husband and raped Hannah," Asta reveled.

"WHAT?!" Gramps exclaimed.

Asta nodded.

"Yes, and I was downstairs and held at gunpoint with four Germans as I heard her pleads and screams," Asta said. Her voice began to break.

He held Asta in his arms. She began to weep quietly.

"Your eyes betray you Ken for I have seen the way you look at Hannah and she looks at you," she said. She looked into his eyes.

He sighed deeply and began to counter.

"Your daughter is the first girl I have met that wasn't like the ones at home. As a member of the resistance and as a solider I would lay down my life before I have harm come to you or her," he stated. He spoke from the heart.

"Thank you," she replied softly.

He kissed her on the head.

"Always," he replied softly.

"I will let you sleep now," she said. She got off the bed.

"Good night," he said.

"Good night," Asta repeated.

After Asta left his room he could feel his heart racing in anger against Karl. However, he knew that if he stayed angry right now he wouldn't be able to sleep so he let it go, for now.

The next morning he confronted Karl in his office and threw him up against the wall.

"What the fuck?! Yes I raped Hannah! Why the fuck do you care?!" Karl yelled. Gramps held him up against the wall.

"I am their guest! "You son of a bitch! If you so much as look at her again I will kill you!" Gramps yelled angrily.

Karl pushed Gramps off him and whipped out his luger pistol from the holster on his hip. He cocked it and pointed it at Gramps.

Gramps scoffed.

"You don't got the balls to shoot me!" Gramps taunted.

"I have killed men before Jap I wouldn't mind adding one more to that count!" he countered.

Gramps swiftly took the weapon from Karl's hand by cupping his at the bottom of Karl's and twisting it until the SS officer let go of the pistol. Gramps then pushed him up against the wall and grabbed the pistol on the floor. By the time Karl was ready to swing at him he stuffed the business end of the luger right in the German's face.

"What are you gonna do? Shoot me?" he said. He panted.

"Don't tempt me Karl," Gramps replied steaming with anger.

After a tense moment Gramps ejected the magazine and pulled the slide back, sending the chambered round flying in the air. He caught the airborne round and set it on his desk. He then shoved the empty pistol back at Karl.

Without exchanging a single word but just glaring at each other Karl stormed off. After Gramps had calmed down a bit he realized that he may have just blown his own cover.

"Shit!" Gramps whispered aloud.

The memory of how Grandpa's emotions nearly blew his cover, reminded me of how I too once did. I am a very cautious and private person however, like Gramps I have a major weakness, being impulsive. We often react emotionally rather than thinking upon the right response. I had an extremely rough time with school and school work. So much so that I hated nearly every minute of it and did everything I could to get out of it. I was always angry and secretive. I didn't fit with the other students in my entire time in school due to my interests being in a totally different universe from them.

Despite my best efforts at keeping a normal emotional front I would blow up at other students for the tiniest things. I was so fuckin' miserable! I was sent often to counselor's offices. With them I would entertain and bond with them over all kinds of stories. Then I began to talk story and bond with other teachers and staff. This trick wasn't something I came up with, no it was a secret weapon devised by Grandpa. He, a master storyteller instilled into me the art and while I was unaware he knew that absolutely no one is immune to the influence of a good story. Growing up in an old family where all you see is old folks I felt at ease being around adults because that's who I was around with all the time. So, in taking story and bonding with them they would pass me in assignments I should have failed on. Sure they would mark with red pen for mistakes but that's where their help ended. See, in story assignments and just simply talking with them they began to overlook the mistakes, rather go for how it was written they went by the story.

The rest of the day went without a single mention of the incident and Gramps went home. As soon as he went home he told George what he did and boy, was the Englishman livid.

"Are you fuckin' mental?!" George screamed. He got up from the armchair and threw his book in the air.

"I know, I know lower your goddamn voice!" Gramps hissed.

"Jesus Christ! Well, that derails the extraction plans! Way to fuckin' go Ken!" George remarked angrily.

"What is the exfil plan?" Gramps asked, surprised.

"Originally had planned a single car wreck and when it would explode it would render the occupant unidentifiable," he said. He calmed down.

"Ah well we still could do something like that perhaps I made up with Karl over drinks and then I crash, the car blows up and the bodies are barbequed so no can identify them," Gramps replied. He poured himself a stiff drink.

"Yes, and I have though up a way to get Asta and Hannah out as well. As gas leaked in the house it was ignited by the fire from the fireplace," George explained. He pointed to the fireplace.

"Brilliant brah. Just brilliant. So, what's the rest of the plan?" Gramps replied. He twisted the cap back onto the bottle.

"Well, after we have staged everything the four of us will be hidden in a resistance boat bound for Stockholm. Once in Sweden we are to board a plane headin' to London where Winnie will meet us," George reveled. He motioned with his hands for the bottle.

"Outstanding," Gramps remarked and handed him the bottle.

George unscrewed the cap, threw it on the table and drank directly from the bottle. He drank the bottle dry before setting it down on the table. In a not too distant future Gramps would find out how George was able to drink an over half full bottle. He suspected that George was or beginning to be an alcoholic. People handle stress differently and well Gramps guessed drinking was the Englishman's way. Gramps said nothing to him nor to Winnie. The way Gramps saw it we all have demons to fight he just hoped that the cure for George's didn't get Gramps killed.

The night before their escape Gramps apologized to Karl over the incident and invited him over to the house for dinner and drinks. Then sometime in the middle of the dinner he gave a signal to George with his eyes. George and Gramps got up and George flew Karl to the ground and held him as Gramps choked him to death. Once Gramps couldn't feel a pulse on Karl he let go and then the group was off to stage the car wreck. They stuck the two bodies in the driver and front passenger side of the car before they rigged it to blow. Once they got back home they rigged the house to blow and with bags in hand they drove to Copenhagen Harbor. Once there an old man met with them and took them aboard a large fishing boat. They stayed hidden in some secret compartment in the boat until they reached Swedish waters. After that the old man gave the all clear and then the group went on deck. Some hours later they docked into the harbor in Stockholm.

Chapter 11

Goodbye Denmark, Hello London

Before the group got off they told the old man thank you and good bye.
The old man was indeed a brave guy and like many of the Danish people,
delighted to help out to undermine the Germans in anyway and every way
they could. Once at the harbor a car arrived to drive them to the airfield.
Like clockwork once at the airfield they hopped onto an airplane and flew to
London. A car greeted them at the airfield in London and from there they
were driven to a hotel. The girls got out and were escorted to their rooms by
a few SOE agents that George knew. George and Gramps stayed in the car
and were driven to a hospital.

"Okay Ken this is where I get off. Adam here will drive you to Winnie,"
George informed.

"Will I ever see you again?" Gramps asked.

"Probably. Good luck mate," he said with his hand stretched out.

"Likewise buddy," Gramps replied. They shook hands.

George got out of the car and it sped off. Gramps wouldn't see George
until a fateful day in May 1945. However, we will get to that later now
where were we ah yes London. London in 1944 was baring the scars of
being bombed relentlessly from the Germans for many years. There were

many armed soldiers around the city and more so than most at Grandpa's destination, Windsor Castle. They drove in; Gramps got out of the car and was escorted to a room. The escort knocked on the door and the door locks clicked open. His escort opened the door and closed it behind Gramps as he got inside the room. The room looked all decorated and here sitting in front of him was not only Winnie but King George VI, the reigning monarch of the British Empire.

"Ken this is King George VI of the British Empire," Winnie introduced.

"Your majesty Captain Kinjiro Kabazawa. It is a true honor to meet you." Gramps said. He bowed.

"Yes, y- you know I- I have heard many tales about you Captain Kabazawa," he said. He stuttered a bit.

'So, it is true about his stuttering.' Gramps thought.

"Thank you your majesty it's a great honor to hear that," Gramps said trying to conceal his smile.

"I must say Ken you are full of surprises. You survived Copenhagen with your cover intact, sent our vital intel to the British and aided fighters of the Danish resistance." Winnie stated. He listed Grandpa's achievements over the past year.

"Thanks Winnie," Gramps replied with a smile.

"You will be decorated with medals to commemorate your immense courage and sacrifice," King George VI stated flawlessly without stammer.

"Thank you King George VI. Perhaps you should just come out with it instead of trying to fill me up before ya do," Gramps remarked. He cracked his neck.

The King chucked.

"Oh I see why you like him Winnie. I do now as well," the King remarked flawlessly without stuttering. He turned to Winnie and then back to Gramps.

"Thanks I think," Gramps replied and glanced over to Winnie.

"You said you wanted to kill Nazis, hmm? Well now you will get your chance. You are headin' to the front. The Eastern Front to be exact," Winnie said with a grin.

"What? I thought I was to join up with the American forces as part of the new all Japanese American unit, 442?" Gramps said, surprised.

"Is there anything you haven't heard of my boy?" Winnie remarked.

"Apparently yes," Gramps answered.

"Josef Stalin the Russian Premier has gotten wind of you and wants you," Winnie reveled. His mood turned a bit more serious.

"What does that Russian tyrant want with me?" Gramps asked puzzled.

"Ah so I take it you've heard of him?" King George VI inquired.

"Yes, I have enough to know, excuse my language for he is not one to fuck with. Or over for that matter," Gramps said.

"Yes, well the mission is simple you are to be dropped into Ukraine via parachute. There you will meet up with a unit of the 1st Ukrainian Front. Once you are with them they will radio in that you made it alive. You objective aside from not getting killed is to get intel about what the Soviets are up to," Winnie laid out without missing a beat.

"How will I get word you?" Gramps asked. He soaked it all up.

"Well, unless it is damn important, you don't. You just hold onto it and fill us in later. Now, Stalin will suspect that you are a spy for the U.S. and since we are all allies it is better if you don't communicate." the King said.

"Sounds good. What's my cover?" Gramps asked. He yawned.

"You are just another over eager Yank who want to kill ever Swastika waving Nazi bastard he sees," Winnie said with a grin.

Gramps laughed.

"Is that what you think of me Gentlemen?" Gramps posed.

"Well, I know for a fact that there is some part of you that is," he replied.

He looked at Gramps.

"When you have seen first-hand what they have done, I don't think you could be anything else. When do I leave?" Gramps replied trying to conceal his anger.

"Ten days from tomorrow," the King replied. He scratched his nose.

"Do your best boy, for that red bastard will try to turn you. Do all you can to resist," Winnie said. He pointed his finger at Gramps.

Gramps nodded.

"I will Winnie," Gramps replied.

"Oh and don't think of heading back to the hotel. The girls have been moved to a safe house in the countryside," Winnie said.

"Why the hell did you do that?!" Gramps angrily spat.

"For the same reason you got them out of Denmark, protection," he replied. He glared at Gramps.

Gramps groaned and rolled his eyes.

"I understand. Make damn sure they will be taken care of and protected," Gramps stated. He trembled in anger.

"Yes, I will see to it personally," Winnie answered with a nod.

"As will I," the King said.

"Well if that is all," Gramps said. He stood up.

"Oh yes I almost forgot," Winnie said. He pulled out a book from his bag.

"What is it?" Gramps asked. He handed the book to him.

"This is an English to Russian language book. Study up lad," he said. He tapped Grandpa's shoulder.

"Will do thanks Gentlemen," Gramps said. He tried his best to smile.

"You are dismissed Captain," The King said.

Gramps bowed to the King and shook hands with Winnie then he left. Once back into the car they drove to a safe house somewhere in London from Windsor.

"No one is living in here but it has been well kept," Adam said. He unlocked the door.

The house was a simple four bedroom house, furnished with a small yard.

"All of the surrounding houses have been evacuated due to bombings," He said.

"So, no neighbors?" Gramps asked, surprised. He looked at him.

"None whatsoever," he replied with a smile.

"Nice, I like it," Gramps replied with a smile.

"Enjoy your stay Captain," he said. He handed Gramps a key.

"Thanks, I will," Gramps responded. He took the key.

Adam nodded and drove off.

Gramps locked the door, ran up the spiral staircase, found what he believed was the master bedroom and flopped on the bed and fell fast asleep.

When he woke up it was 10AM the next morning. He reset his watch to London time, went downstairs and made himself breakfast. He made eggs and bacon and sunk his teeth into a shiny red apple. Since he was ordered to not to go looking for Hannah in so many words he rummaged around the cabinets for the place they kept the alcohol. As he was doing this he found

150,000 pounds (British currency) in a drawer. He knew why but still he
wanted to see her. Ah young love yes those were some sweet days. He
found it a whole stash of bottles unopened just wanting for him. So, he
decided to get completely shit faced before he went out looking for her. He
pulled a bottle of single malt and got down to drowning his frustrations with
the superb quality brown stuff. He figured that he was being watched so he
decided to wait before he made any attempt to go out and find Hannah. As
he walked through the house he suddenly found himself inside the library of
it. Many books lined the shelves of the large book shelf.
"Stevenson, Dickens, Wells, Shakespeare, Barrie, Verne, Tolkien,
Twain," Gramps said. He ran his finger pass the books.
"Hell of a collection," he said. He pulled Moby Dick off the shelf.
He opened the book and to his amazement it was a first edition.
"Oh shit these are all first editions!" He exclaimed.
He got comfy on an old leather armchair and got to reading. He was
nearly finished with the book before the sun sat at four in the afternoon. He
was so drunk that right after he finished the book he instantly fell asleep. He
dreamed of Hannah at the Christmas dinner in Copenhagen and just
laughing. It was one of those dreams that you just don't want to wake from
because when you do it disappears. Nevertheless, Gramps awoke and swore
loudly before standing up stretching out his legs. It was pitch black and so
him being him he decided to grab a flashlight and jacket to go exploring his
new surroundings.
He went outside and started to walk down the street. It was super creepy
because there was absolutely no noise but dead silence. Some of the houses
were bombed out and in ruin which made the place feel even creepier. He
dared to venture in the remains of the questionable homes and found lives
interrupted by war. He figured that some people died in these houses but
never found any bodies. Once he got tired he walked back to the house and
took a nice hot bath. After that he made some dinner and went to bed. The
next day he decided he was going into town and was in need of some
company. He looked for something to drive but found not a car or truck but
a motorcycle. It was a Harley Davidson that the United States had sent the
British prior to Pearl Harbor being lit up. The British military used the HDs
bikes as well as English made ones like BSA and Norton. Prior to that he
only had ridden a motorcycle once before and that was back home on Kauai.

Gramps racked his brain on remembering how to work one of these bikes and after 15 minutes he rode out into town like a pro. He wore a British Captain's Dress uniform with an overcoat for warmth. He parked outside of a small club. He walked in the entire place went dead silent. Strong scents of tobacco and stale beer filled his nose. A dozen or so heavy streams of tobacco clouds made his eyes water a bit. He sat down at an empty table and a young beautiful girl took his order. She had long brown hair and emerald green eyes. He was extremely taken back by her gorgeous looks as well as her other nice uh... assets.

"What do you want Captain?" she asked in a semi grumpy mood.

"Uh well, what do you recommend?" Gramps asked. he couldn't take his eyes off of her.

"I recommend a pint of ale," she said with a sigh.

"Good I'll have a pint of ale," he replied with a smile.

She nodded and went off. From the table he could see her getting behind the counter and filling up a large glass.

"Please continue. Don't let me be the damper on the festivities," Gramps remarked. He looked around the bar.

Just like that the men nodded and an American GI on the piano began playing again and all the different conversations resumed. Apparently what had happened was that Gramps was the highest ranking person in the room as well as being a Japanese-American. The men didn't snap to attention but they were still giving him dirty glances. When the waitress came back with his ale he told her to sit.

"Does this always happen to you?" she asked. She side eyed him.

"Does what?" He asked. He took a sip of the foamy glass.

"The room dies," she explained.

"Oh that. No that is certainly a first," he replied with a smile.

"Oh. So, where are you stationed?" she inquired.

"Uh- close," he replied nervously. He took another sip.

"You must be new otherwise I would have seen you before," she said. She stared at him, trying to figure him out.

"Spot on. Yes, I am new I just got in yesterday and will be here for 10 days or so," he said. He massaged his shoulder.

"10 days? You must be with special services," she said half joking.

"Perhaps I am. What time do you finish here?" He posed. He took another sip.

"Midnight. Why?" she asked, curiously. She continued to look at him.

"I was thinkin' you could accompany me back to my place," he slyly replied.

"I'll think about it," she sensually remarked with a killer smile to match.

Gramps nodded and she then got back up to serve more thirsty soldiers. He watched her. She was working and more that once they locked eyes together. She had this spark in her eyes he didn't know what it was but it was something. He nursed his ale for quite some time before he finished it and ordered a pint of Guinness. Two hours later she finished her shift and they walked out together.

"I never got your name," Gramps remarked. He looked at her.

"I never got yours," she countered. She looked at him.

He chuckled.

Perhaps Gramps was trying to cram the hole that Hannah had left or he just was leaping without thinking. He was least you forget a teenager after all. He wanted to let loose and have fun in a brand new place. Be careful what you wish for? Yeah if he only listened to that, but again that's just not his style. No, he always gotta learn everything the hard way as usual. This is a trait I had the misfortune of inheriting from him.

"It's Kinjiro," Gramps answered with a half grin.

"Avery," She replied with a grin.

"Well, hop on Avery," he said. He got on the bike.

"Is this yours?" Avery asked, wide eyed.

"Yeah kind of," he replied with a chuckle.

They hopped on and he gunned the engine to the house. When they got to the house he killed the engine and they got off the bike.

"This is home for now," he stated. He looked at the house and back at her.

"Wow," Avery whispered, in awe.

"Come on you ain't seen nothin' yet," he remarked with a smile.

He unlocked the house doors and flipped on the lights as they walked in.

"Holy shit!" She exclaimed.

"Come on I'll give you the nickel tour," he remarked. He tossed his head to the side and gave a smile.

Avery laughed.

Gramps showed her all the rooms. He mimicked the voice of that of a game show host including the library where like him Avery marveled at the books that lined the walls. She smiled and laughed all through the grand house. She truly had a sexy smile and a wicked laugh it was cute and well a great weakness for him.

"Now here is the master bedroom," he said. He continued with his game show host voice.

Avery pushed him onto the bed and he went down face first.

You can use your imagination as to what happened next.

Although, his heart ached for Hannah he knew that it would be wise not to go looking for her. He had average teenage problems while playing a very incredible adult role. Heartbreak at any age is something that one will do whatever to avoid feeling. He didn't want to make Winnie look bad so he let it go as much as he could.

The story of Avery and Gramps came back to me when I was drunk in a bar in Pittsburgh of all places early one morning. I had the dumb idea to take a private jet to the home of my cousin's favorite football team the Steelers from get this Arlington, Virginia. I had a few drinks in me already, got into a cab and for some reason I had Pittsburgh on my mind, so I blurted out for him to drive me to the airport.

Once at the airport I asked around if anyone knew of a private jet heading to Pittsburgh. After coming up empty for a bit an a Transportation Security Agent (TSA) worker told me of a private jet heading there soon. I thanked the worker and palmed him a few C-notes. I would later learn that TSA and Airport Security are your best bet for information on private jets. As part of the security arm of all airports across the country it's their job to search and secure every inbound and outbound individual and aircraft. I managed to make my way to the private jet and bribed my way on.

The jet was a very beautiful and expensive Gulfstream G5. In the jet was just one passenger and a pilot. The flight was a short hour long. In that fight I found out that the man's name was Brian, he just turned 33 a few weeks back, born and raised in Giddings, Texas. He served in the army after high school, did three combat tours, was stationed on Oahu for a bit and was a duel major in drama and English literature major of Oxford University. His family came from old money, oil wells. Despite being from money Brian never let it influence him. He was an all-around nice guy who carved out his own path without any favors from his family. The only bad part of him was that womanizer side, but then again most young men are.

Brian and I talked about foods, travels, war stories and life. We even recited several sonnets from the Bard which is something of a miracle for me because I always failed English class when it came to Willie Shakespeare. When we got to the 'burgh I was still pretty drunk and so my memory is still a bit fuzzy but I remember offering to buy Brian a drink. He accepted the offer mostly because he had no plans. We ducked into a bar and one drink turned into 10. The drinks were beers, Coors Lights with water and Reyka Vodka neat on the side. While we were at the bar a group of super-hot sorority girls walked in. One of which had long brown hair and emerald like eyes. Both Brian and I were mesmerized by her. He pulled his dogtags from under his shirt and went over.

Long story short my buddy Brian left the bar with the entire bunch of super-hot sorority girls. While I after downing my last drink, hailed a cab to the airport, bribed my way on a late night flight back to Arlington and snuck back into my hotel.

Chapter 12

The General

When Avery and Gramps woke up they just did well you know what for a few hours. After they began to get hungry he went down stairs to make breakfast. After he made breakfast he looked around for a tray and those silver servers that they have at fine dining restaurants. After rummaging around he found what he was looking for and a napkin. He put everything together and walked up the stairs.

"Breakfast is served Madam," Gramps said in his best English accent. Avery sat up her long brown hair a mess of knots, clapped and laughed. He placed the tray on her lap then dove back into bed and lifted the cover off reveling the spread. Breakfast consisted of bacon, ham, eggs, apple slices, toast with butter and jam, and milk.

"Not bad with the accent. You know I have never had breakfast in bed," Avery said seductively.

"Well, now you can scratch that off your list," Gramps replied softly. They kissed.

"Yes, I certainly can," she said. She giggled with glee.

"God, you are so beautiful," Gramps remarked. He stared at her.

"Thanks honey," Avery said. Her cheeks turned a light shade of red. After they finished eating they got dressed and ready for the day. They hopped back on the bike and drove into town. Avery showed Gramps around the city. He parked the bike and they walked hand in hand through the parks and gardens. He never thought of her as a rebound but another love and warm light in a world ravaged with war and death. They watched

the sunset together and kissed as it sat over the horizon. After that they ate
dinner at a restaurant and dropped her off at her place.
"I'll pack a bag and when my shift is over I'll come over to your place,"
Avery said.
"Sounds fantastic," Gramps replied. They kissed.
"Are you coming to the club?" she asked.
"No, I'm afraid not. I have to get some work done," Gramps replied.
Avery nodded.
"See you later tonight baby," Avery said. She began to walk insider her
apartment building.
"Oh, I am in some deep shit now," he remarked once she was out of
sight.
Gramps started the bike and drove back home. Once home he started to
compile notes on Avery and wanted to run a background check to make sure
that she wasn't a spy for the Nazis or anyone else. In England, especially in
London there were operatives or spies from Germany, America, and Soviet
Union and of course the English themselves. He hoped that Avery wasn't an
agent or unwilling pawn working for them. If she was with, British Security
Service, Mi5, England's domestic intel agency then he was in for the ass
chewing of the century. Mi5 is like the Federal Bureau of Investigation
(FBI) in the United States. They handle all spying in house or in the country.
However, due to the war their reach expanded to International as well.
As Gramps finished writing down all the info he had on Avery he
decided to get a bottle of something strong. He found a bottle of vintage
wine, opened it and drink straight from the bottle. It was a bottle of red wine
vintage 1909. He had never cared much for wine primarily because he
couldn't tell the difference between an aged bottle and one from two years
ago. In his mind if got him tanked it did the job. He decided to pull out the
English to Russian book that Winnie gave him and began to read it. He read
the book until he heard a car engine pull up in front of the house. He then
put the book and notes away in his bag hidden out of sight. After that he
made his way to the front door and opened it.
"Hi baby," Avery said. They kissed.
Avery had a small luggage bag and Gramps took it from her hand as they
walked into the house arm in arm. As soon as they got into the house he
swooped her off her feet and carried her up the stairs. They drank and sat on

the bed, talked and other things. This 'intimate' time with Avery continued for the rest of his time in London.

One night after they had drank a handful of bottles dry they talked for hours until the sun came up. They chatted about her childhood growing up in London. It was not after these talks that he concluded that Avery was not an agent nor was she under anyone's thumb as one. Her father Lewis was a First World War veteran who served in the trenches in France as a cavalry officer and was a banker. Her mother Jenna was a baker whose specialty was pastries. Avery was the middle child of three sisters. Her eldest sister Mary was married to a charming Royal Air Force Major and lived in Stoke-on-Trent, Staffordshire. Her youngest sister Emma married a young Royal Marine and lived in Manchester. Growing up they had a long line of dogs mainly Golden Retrievers.

"How about you? What did Kenny do as a young lad?" Avery asked. She looked right into his eyes.

"Well, I grew up on farm kind of – a dairy. We had cows, dogs of all sorts, and horses. I along with others would milk the cows by hand and bottle the milk. My father like yours is good with numbers and so he works in the office with them. My brothers both older and younger wok at the dairy doing the same as I, tending to the animals. My mother, a seamstress who also washes clothes to get extra money but otherwise she takes care of the house. My sisters are still in school with the exception of one who is both working and in school but the rest are not working yet," Gramps reveled. He looked at the walls. He tried to picture everything he just described.

"I never pictured you as a farm boy," Avery remarked with a hint of surprise in her voice.

Gramps chuckled.

"Yeah well, I am," he said. He cracked a half grin and He looked at her.

"So, the one thing I don't get is how a dairy boy from Kauai gets from there to here?" she asked. She pushed her bangs to the side.

"Well.. that is a complicated story to say the least. One that is still unfolding as we speak," he said. He searched to find the right words.

"Am I in it- the story?" she teased with a seductive smile.

"Yes, you are," he replied. They kissed.

"Good. I would be greatly disappointed if I wasn't," she said softly.

"So, where do you want to go today?" He asked with a smile.

"Hmm I don't know you pick," Avery countered.

"Okay. How about a stroll through London?" He asked.

"Perfect. Absolutely perfect," she said. They kissed once more.

After the couple had made love once again they got dressed and headed out. They hopped on the bike and they road into town. Gramps parked his bike at a restaurant and from there they wondered the streets hand in hand for hours. As the sun began to set they went back home and he made dinner.

He turned out all the lights and they ate only by candle light. It was extremely romantic to say the least. After dessert, they went upstairs, drank, made love, and read books side by side in bed before falling asleep. His last night in London there was a knock on the door late at night. He pulled his 45 pistol, cocked it and slowly inched his way down the stairs to the door. When he opened it, he was incredibly surprised to see General Dwight D. Eisenhower nicknamed Ike standing outside.

"I am so sorry General," Gramps said. He clicked the safety on and lowered the pistol.

"That is all right son. I'd do the same," Eisenhower replied with a grin.

Eisenhower walked in and Gramps closed the door behind him.

"Please sit. You want anything to drink or eat?" Gramps asked. He automatically went into the role of a host.

"Nothing to eat but something strong to drink would be nice, thank you," he responded with a smile.

"Please have a seat," Gramps said. The men sat on a couple of armchairs in the parlor.

"Is everything all right down there Ken?" Avery hollered from the bedroom.

Eisenhower and Gramps looked at each other awkwardly.

"Hop to it then," he said with a half grin.

"Will you excuse me General?" Gramps asked nervously. He got up.

The General nodded and Gramps went upstairs.

"Avery darling it's all right," Gramps said, trying to conceal his nervousness.

"Who is it?" she asked, curiously.

"General Eisenhower," Gramps replied. He sucked in his lips.

"You are joking!" she floored, exclaimed.

"No, he's right downstairs sitting on the chair next to the fireplace," he said.

"Wow. Can I meet him?" she asked wide eyed.

"Later. I have a feeling he has a lot to discuss with me," he answered.

"Oaky, I'll just be up there keeping bed warm for you," she said.

He nodded with his cheeks turning a light shade of pink.

Gramps came back down the stairs and fixed a drink for him and the General.

"Getting to know the locals now Captain?" the General remarked.

"Yes, quite intimately at that sir," Gramps answered with this big goofy grin and sat back down.

The General chucked.

"Please call me Dwight," he said with a nod.

"Thank you Dwight," Gramps said with a nod.

"You have certainly earned that right," he remarked. He looked at Gramps.

"Thank you. You may call me Ken," Gramps replied with a half grin.

Dwight nodded.

"How you holdin' up Ken?" Dwight asked.

"All right I guess," Gramps said. He shrugged his shoulders.

"Yeah well if it makes you feel any better you have survived worse before," he remarked. He took a sip from his glass.

Gramps laughed and nodded.

"Yeah, it's just that Winnie and King George have asked me to gather as much information as I can while I'm runnin' with the Russians," Gramps vented.

"Yes, and I am here to tell you that Franklin and I back it," he said and shifted his weight around.

"Do you now?" Gramps remarked. He side eyed Dwight.

"Yes. Although we are not as crazed on the Soviets as Churchill we, the U.S. Government, has deemed them the next threat. I mean what communism and democracy stand for are two vastly different things. This partnership with the Soviets was never meant to last anyway," he reveled.

He took another sip from his glass.

"Yeah Winnie said something about the Soviets having agents in both British and American intel," Gramps said. He took a sip from his glass.

"Yeah that is being taken care of by Wild Bill," he said. He rubbed his eyes.

"Wild Bill?" Gramps asked, surprised.

"Yeah uh Will Donovan head of the OSS," he said.

"Oh yeah I have heard of him," Gramps said. He took a sip from his glass.

"So, now that the stakes are much higher an order was issued that all documents, photos and evidence of your existence during this war will be collected and destroyed immediately after the war ends. Those who know of you that are still alive when this war is over will be sworn to secrecy, " he informed.

"So, what? I'm the fuckin' golden goose?" Gramps cracked.

"No. You're the fuckin' platinum goose," he threw back.

"Wow. And here I thought I was just gonna kill Krauts," Gramps sarcastically said with a laugh.

"Yeah you get to do that too," Dwight replied with a grin.

"All right is that all Dwight?" Gramps asked.

"A few last things Roosevelt is playing you extremely close to the vest not even the vice president knows about you. So, do your duty and don't for the love of all things holy get yourself caught and or killed," he said sternly.

"Yes, sir," Gramps replied with gusto.

"Good. Now about the girl," he said. His mood lightened once again.

"Which one?" Gramps quipped with a great big goofy grin plastered on his face.

Dwight began to laugh hard and Gramps joined in.

"Oh. No but seriously, uh I can take care of them-relocate them to the States, protection and money. No questions asked," he said serious once again.

"I am sensing a catch," Gramps remarked. He scratched his head.

"Yeah uh you can never see or contact them again," he said. He scratched his cheek.

Gramps nodded.

"How fast can you set it up?" Gramps asked.

"Immediately," he replied.

"Good, I'll bring her down," Gramps said with a nod.

He nodded.

Gramps walked back up the stairs and told Avery to get dressed into something suitable for their unannounced guest. After she did the couple walked back down the stairs arm in arm.

"Avery, this is General Dwight Eisenhower," Gramps introduced.

"How do you do Ma'am?" he said. He stretched his hand out.

"Uh fine and you General?" Avery nervously replied all smiles. She shook hands.

"Now, darling the General wants you to go with him," Gramps stated.

"Will you be coming along dear?" she asked. She looked at Gramps then back at Dwight.

"Yes, I will be right behind you," Gramps lied with a smile.

Avery and Gramps kissed for the last time ever before he watched them hop into a car and take off. That was the last time he ever saw either of them until another war broke and he was back the service only this time it was official, kinda. Dwight, Gramps would hear from again in 1951, seven years later. Later on, he would hear things about Avery and would eventually find about her tragic fate in 1952. It was at this time in 1952 he found out under who she was truly operating under. She was handpicked by Winnie as an SOE agent to make sure he was not duped by an Allied or Axis agent. She would later report back to the Prime Minister that Gramps was spilling everything to her a complete stranger very easily and openly.

It was further reported that in her professional opinion he was far to young and inexperienced to ever make an effective agent. That was of course until she had been told the full extent of his activities. That info made her turn a complete 180 though she still stood by the decision that he was too young for the role he had been forced into.

After the war was over it was agreed by the British Government that no teenager should ever be selected into an intelligence role again. That is unless the situation calls an individual the only choice between the continued flight of the Union Jack over Great Britain vs someone else's.

Avery's identity was tragically betrayed by members of the so called 'Cambridge Five' spy ring. The spy ring took its name from Cambridge University in England, where all five members attended once. The members were approached by Soviet Intelligence while at Cambridge University in the 1930s, before the war. During the war they all rose to high positions deep in the echelons of the British Government and Military. All the while they passed on closely held secrets to the Soviets. After the war they continued to spy for the Soviets. They were discovered in 1951 after the first two fled to Russia.

The Cambridge Five betrayed so many good men and women in their treachery. Avery was then an agent in Budapest, Hungary. Hungary was a communism country under the Soviet Union from 1945-1989. She was discovered, tortured, tried and executed in 1947. Her remains were brought home to her native England in 2000.

Avery was what you would now call a "rebound" but he never saw her as that. The love Gramps shared with her was not a fleeting moment or fling. No, it was the kind that stays with a person. He couldn't sleep after Avery left so he decided to pack up his stuff in his duffel. At four in the morning a car came by to pick him up. It drove him to a field where a small military plane waited. The Japanese American kid was briefed on where he was to be dropped in Ukraine and refreshed on how to use the parachute. Once that was over he was loaded into the plane and they were off.

Gramps would eventually learn much later that the real reason behind the Germans exceptional hospitality excluding the beating he received was simply because they wanted to keep their Japanese Ally happy. The Germans thought of the Japanese as inferior people like the ones they were killing by the droves but they dared not say it in the faces of the Japanese. The Japanese after all were neither tall, nor blond, nor did we have blue eyes all the characteristics of the so-called Germany Aryan Master Race.

The Japanese though were even more fanatical and brutal fighters which made the Germans shudder in fear. That is why they never dared to even accidently disrespect them for on top of not having lost a war in thousands of years they beat the Imperial Russians. Plus, the thought of having to fight a war on three fronts spelled out certain doom of a thousand year domination. Not to mention the fact that after the Italian Campaign concluded in defeat the Japanese were the last remaining ally of the Germans.

The next time Gramps would be in Europe would be in 1952 and he would visit among some new places, some old like Denmark and Jolly Old England. It would be a new adventure and a whole new world as well. However, I'm getting a bit ahead of myself so bear with me while I get there.

Chapter 13

Eastern Hell

As Gramps flew to Ukraine he couldn't help but be reminded about the last time he had a parachute strapped to his back. It was immensely disastrous as the plane was hit and both Jimmy the pilot and he had to bail out above the Filipino jungle. He was clear he wasn't nervous but he just had the thought in his head and one that stayed with him until it was time to jump. He opened the door and the first thing that struck him was how incredibly cold the air was. He knew it was still winter and there was snow everywhere but he was not prepared for how cold it would be. He was so caught off guard he nearly lost his footing and almost fell out of the door. He was dressed in all black with a large fur lined jacket. He hooked on to the line above and as soon as the red light turned green he was out the door. He was armed with a German made MP40 submachine gun the very same one he had from Denmark. He was also armed with two side arms his Luger P08 and a Browning Hi- Power, which looked like a .45 but chambered a 9 millimeter courtesy of the Brits. He had a snub nose revolver on his inner right ankle. He also had a Samurai Sword that he had gotten from the Japanese in his time in the Philippines. He was truly a walking armory! The sword was strapped tightly to his chest and he was quite nervous that he would break his jaw on it while he was in freefall before he would pull his chute.

Gramps had many more weapons and treasures that he collected but they were being held back in London for him. The instruction for them was simple should he survive it was to be mailed to Kauai and that included whatever else he collected from all the places he had been including where he was now the Eastern Front. If he was to fall in combat the instructions stayed the same the stuff would be sent home regardless and uninspected. As he free fell from the sky the cold wind felt like daggers stabbing at his skin over and over again. As he pulled his parachute he felt a strong breeze and it pushed him off course. As he tried to steer the parachute the Japanese American GI made eye contact with a small but sizeable force of about 20 *Wehrmacht* or regular German Army soldiers.

As the Germans began to yell and open fire on Gramps he tried to swing his left arm to grab his MP40 while steering the parachute with his right. He got a hold of his weapon and fired he killed six Germans and then lost grip of the gun. He hit and tangled up on two trees about 40 feet in the air. As the Germans began to swarm the area he pulled out a few grenades and threw them down as a present for them. As the grenades went off he could hear and see them be blown up. He pulled his pistols and opened fire from above. He killed all but four of them before they began to retreat and suddenly the place erupted with at least two dozen machine guns blasting.

"Oh shit!" Gramps exclaimed.

Gramps knew that the SS would kill any German soldier who retreated he frantically ejected the empty magazines from the pistols and put in fully loaded ones. As more figures began to emerge closer below me he pointed his guns at them. However, they were dressed in camouflaged white uniforms and that threw him off.

"Captain! Do not fire!" a distinctive female voice yelled in English with a thick European accent.

The voice had a heavy Russian accent and he soon realized that it was the Soviet force he was to meet up with.

"Identify yourselves!" Gramps yelled back with his guns still trained on them.

"Sergeant Anna 13th Army 1st Ukrainian front!!" the women yelled.

"Oh, got it!" Gramps yelled and rolled his eyes. He lowered his guns and placed them back in the holster.

Gramps reached for his sword to cut the parachute cord. Once he was free he began to carefully climb down the tree. As his boots hit the ground he greeted the Soviet troops that surrounded him.

"You shoot good American Cowboy," Anna remarked in English with a thick Eastern European accent.

"Thanks. You guys don't do so bad either," Gramps replied. He sized them up.

"Come on let's head back to the outpost," Anna said.

Anna then shouted a command in Russian and they began walking.

"You speak good English for a Russian," Gramps remarked. They walked.

"Well, I'm not a Russian I'm a Ukrainian," she replied. She angrily glared at him a moment.

"Oh sorry. My mistake," Gramps apologized.

She nodded.

The squad of Soviets was eight guys and one girl, Anna. By the looks of things she seemed to be calling all the shots. Anna was a beauty with shimmy blond hair and these great dark blue eyes. Her face looked like Paulette Goddard, the silent film actress and Charlie Chaplin's ex-wife. She was quite beautiful and Gramps couldn't take his eyes off of her the entire walk to the outpost. The men in the squad spoke to each other in Russian but he couldn't understand it, not yet.

"How did you learn to speak English so good?" Gramps asked. He pulled out a pair of sunglasses undamaged from his breast pocket.

"Oh my uh mother used to teach me and my brothers. She learned it during her days as a University student," Anna answered.

"Oh," Gramps replied and nodded.

Gramps and Anna talked for the entire time and whatever it was they just seemed to click. When they got to the outpost Gramps was introduced to the commanding officer Major Marko. It was a bit difficult because Anna had to translate for them because the Major was just beginning to learn English.

"Captain Kinjiro Kabazawa meet my second in command Lieutenant Alexi," Anna translated.

Alexi and Gramps shook hands and exchanged greetings.

"Lieutenant Alexi is also my brother," Anna translated.

"Nice," Gramps replied.

"I will let you get familiar with brothers and sisters in arms. Then, Anna will show you to your quarters," she translated.

Gramps nodded.

"Thank you Major," Gramps said. He nodded to him.

Major Marko returned the nod and he walked off.

As Anna introduced Gramps to the other Soviet soldiers he was presented with a Soviet winter wear uniform called a Telogreika, a fur hat called an Ushanka and a pair of Soviet combat boots by LT Alexi. Gramps was so grateful that they had or was pretending to accept him.

"Like my first day of middle school in Waimea," I interrupted.

"Yeah, just about," Gramps said with a laugh.

This also was the time that Gramps was introduced to Natalia. She would become a great friend and the future wife of one of his buddies later. After all the introductions were finished Anna showed him to his quarters, which was a large single man hut. He laid his gear on the ground and changed into the Soviet gear. He put on the boots he thought how the hell did they know his size? He knew better than to question that so he didn't bring it up. After he had finished changing he pulled the English to Russian book that Winnie had given him and began to read it.

He must have fallen asleep at some point because the next thing he knew he was being woken up by Anna.

"Get up Captain Kinjiro Kabazawa!" Anna shouted and shook him.

"Wha-what is it?" Gramps asked. He rubbed his eyes.

"We have been called up to aid our comrades in battle," she said. She walked out of his hut.

As Gramps walked out Natalia threw him a PPSH M1941 submachine gun and a bag of drum magazines for it. The PPSH M1941 looked similar to the American made Thompson Submachine gun. The other similarity was that it took pistol rounds used magazines in both stick and drum form. It stood out with a ridicules firing rate of 1000 rounds per minute. The other major standout feature was that there were air holes all along either side of the barrel preferably to keep the gun cool. In later years the gun would be given a fitting nickname as a result of its ridiculous rate of fire, 'the burp gun.'

"*Spasibo* (Thanks)," Gramps said in Russian. He pulled out the ammo drum to check it and stuck it back on.

The girls chucked and they walked to where Marko was addressing the crowd of Soviet troops.

"You understand Russian?" Anna asked wide eyed.

"No, I just learned from a book," Gramps replied. He tapped his chest.

Anna translated his answer to Natalia and she resounded back in Russian.

"Natalia asked if you would be willing to teach her English?" Anna translated.

"Yes. It would be great honor," Gramps said with a smile.

Anna translated his answer and her response.

"She says thank you," Anna said with a smile.

Gramps nodded.

One of the very first terms Gramps learned was 'Hitlerite' it meant everything German. It also meant every German who didn't take up arms against Hitler. He was corrected by Anna when he spoke about his experience in Denmark and used the term 'Nazi.' Nazi or the National Socialists Party was originally a political worker's party before the outbreak of the war. However both terms are used in this story. They were extreme right from the get go as racism and hatred as well as the idea of a master race of tall, blond and blue eyed people were what they were all about.

The Soviets got into groups of 20 and as Major Marko yelled commands one by one the groups moved out. When Major Marko got to Grandpa's group he gave commands to Anna who then yelled them out to the other men in their group and they were off to face the Germans.

"Major Marko said that although you are the second most senior officer here. But you uh cannot communicate. So, he has instructed me to be your translator until you do," Anna said.

"Ah okay. So what are the instructions?" Gramps said. He studied his weapon for a bit then clicked the safety off his weapon.

"We are to link up with LT Alexi and commence an attack on the German left flank," she revealed with a smile.

As the sounds of small arms fire grew louder and the thunderous booms of the main gun on T-34 Soviet tank Gramps began to get his first taste of the Russian front. As he began to hear German voices clearly to the point he could understand them he got an idea. They came across a squad of Germans and they exchanged fire. He opened up with his weapons and he was in awe of how powerful the Soviet gun was. For every light pull of the trigger there seemed to be three bullets that flew out of its spout. It also made the sound a bit similar to a loud burp.

"Anna!" Gramps shouted in between the gunfire.

"What?!" she yelled back.

Although the Ukrainian and American were right next to each other it was so damn loud that they just shouted back and forth at each other. "Who's the radio man?" Gramps shouted and laid down some lead. He fired his weapon with one hand.

"Private Peter! Why?" Anna yelled back. She fired her weapon.

"Cause I got an idea!" Gramps yelled. He sprayed down three Germans.

Anna yelled for PFC Peter to come over and all of a sudden a German MG-42 machine gun began to roar and fly rounds all over their position.

"Shit! Get down! Gramps yelled. He shielded Anna and they kissed the ground.

Three of their men had been mowed down when that MG-42 opened up and PFC Peter crawled on his belly slowly making his way to them.

As Anna flipped over to face Gramps their eyes met and it was an instant connection. In this moment all other sounds seemed to be muted and even the snow that the bullets made fly upon impact flew in slow motion. As they both were breathing heavily Gramps turned his head to the side and their lips met in their first kiss. Gramps closed his eyes and the feeling was a great rush of pleasure just hit him like a ton of bricks.

"Yowza!" Gramps exclaimed softly. He opened his eyes.

"Oh wow!" Anna said softly with a giggle.

"Comrades!" Private Peter yelled. All the surrounding sounds came back.

"Right. Can you tune into the Hitlerite frequency?" Gramps asked. He got off of Anna.

Gramps extended out his arm and Anna took hold of it as she got up.

Anna translated and the Soviet Private First Class nodded.

PFC Peter bounced his head, messed with the dials and he shouted.

"It's in now what?" Anna asked. She looked at Gramps.

"Watch this," Gramps replied with a large devilish grin that stretched from ear to ear.

Grandpa grabbed the phone part of the radio and began yelling in it in German.

"We are being overrun! Send more troops to the left flank at once!" Gramps screamed in German.

"Who is this?!" a voice yelled in German on the other end.

"This is the Captain you idiot! Now do it!" Gramps angrily screamed in German.

" Uh y -yes, Herr Captain! Sorry Herr Captain!" the voice stammered in German.

Gramps let go of the phone and began to laugh.

"What the hell are you doin'? Do you want to get us all killed?!" Anna yelled. She punched Gramps in the arm hard.

"No. I'm creating a hole. One that Alexi's men can get through and nail the Krauts from behind," Gramps explained and rubbed his arm.

After a moment the words began to sink in to Anna and she responded. "You can speak German?! And didn't care to tell me?" she yelled and hit him once more in the same spot on his arm.

"Ow! Surprise?" Gramps said weakly with a smile. He continued to rub his arm.

As the scores of Germans and their reinforcements began to pour in on Grandpa's position they engaged them. Every so often someone would yell "grenade" and all of them would scramble to find it and get out of the way. One landed right by Grandpa's foot as he was shooting at some Hitlerites and he threw it back and destroyed the MG42. Once they silenced that they charged at the Germans and soon hand to hand combat ensued. To say the scene was a bloodbath was quiet an understatement. People were being stabbed and gutted with bayonets and knives. While other were being bashed with steel helmets and the butts of rifles. There are no words that would come close to describing what Gramps saw and did that day other than total and pure carnage.

Once the battle was over and the Soviets had their little victory they began the time consuming task of searching the dead enemy bodies for intelligence and taking war trophies. As he surveyed the scene Gramps realized that in a way the dark red blood that soaked the snowy grounds reminded him of Shave Ice from back home. For those unfamiliar with the Hawaiian delicacy it's much like a snow cone drenched in flavored syrup.

Yeah it looked like a strawberry flavored shave ice that was drenched generously thick of the sweet syrup. Although, it may look like one DO NOT call shave ice a snow cone when talking to the local residents it will piss them, us off.

After searching all the enemy dead the Soviet group buried their dead respectfully and made a large mountain of weapons. Some of the soldiers swapped weapons in favor of recently liberated hardware. While others had run low on ammo or just wanted to stick the Hitlerites back with their own arms (i.e. Gramps). Personally he preferred the PPSH M1941 as a main weapon and sidearm a variety, semiautomatics and revolvers but mostly the German Luger. Why? Well, for starters how it was shaped perfectly to the human hand is unbelievable. The other thing is that it was so simple to field strip apart, clean, and put back together.

Once all of them was fully locked and loaded it was time to set up camp and celebrate their little victory. Although they had won the small battle the bigger one that they were part of still waged. Maj. Marko had decided that in honor of Grandpa's first victory as a Soviet it was a cause for celebration.

"In times like these you should celebrate as much as you can Captain Kinjiro Kabazawa. Because you never know when it will be your last," Marko stated with a grin.

It truly was a good point and so they found some alcohol the Germans had, cracked it opened and down the hatch it went. Also because of the trick Gramps pulled on the Germans, more Soviets began to accept or at least respect him on some level. After their celebratory antics had come to an end they fought for nearly a month in the harshest winter that Grandpa had experienced up to that time. In the weeks that followed they encircled the Germans which were comprised of six divisions including the 5th SS Panzer Tank Division Wiking. When Gramps found out about the Wiking div he was a bit rattled because it was composed of volunteers from Denmark, Norway, Sweden, Estonia, the Netherlands, and Belgium. He was afraid he would run into Danish Nazis he had met at the Schalburge Corps in Copenhagen. However, the SS was the fanatical and most die-hard of the Nazis so they were to be treated with no mercy whatsoever.

The battle was what some of the few vets the Soviets had told Gramps was that it was much like the Battle of Stalingrad. The Soviets encircled the Germans and nailed them in Stalingrad. Although from what he had read and was now hearing Stalingrad was no walk in the park but a freaking bloodbath. When the dust settled the dead on both sides were estimated to be in the millions. Of that count it included scores of Russian civilians. Once the encirclement was complete then the real fun could begin. They engaged the trapped Nazis and on February 12th they had begun to receive supplied via airdrops.

The Germans were capturing towns and villages in the area which they were trapped in by the Soviets. Civilians would now be caught in deadly crossfire between two enemies that wanted to wipe out one another from the face of the Earth. As ferocious fighting engulfed the towns Anna and Natalia tried to get as many civilians out of the crossfire as possible. They managed to get a mere twenty from two villages, Kormarovka and Shanderovka. They got them safely behind Soviet tanks and then to Red Army troops at the rear. Once the battle was over they would have nothing to go back to. Gramps felt real bad but that's war.

As Gramps engaged the Germans town to town and village to village it was the same every place. Intense and heavy gunfire combined with grenades being thrown everywhere was the scene. Civilians if there were any left were usually caught in the crossfire or took their own lives. It was like a slaughterhouse with the blood soaked grounds and bodies everywhere. The worse times were when the rumblings of a German made Tiger tank came closer. When the main cannon on a Tiger discharged the whole Earth shook as if a giant was roaming. That frightened him more than anything because their armor was incredibly thick it was nearly impossible to take out with a shoulder fired rocket launcher. The only to take them out was four ways, blow the ice and shoot them while they swim, trick them, blow the tracks, or unload the main gun of a Soviet T-34 on a weak spot on the tank.

This time Alexi and Gramps decided the best way to take out the massive German tank was to trick it. Alexi informed his brother to take a unit and distract the tank crew from the front while Alexi and Gramps snuck from the back. Alexi pulled his six shooter, pulled the hammer back softly climbed up on the tank and let lose one round that implanted itself in the back of the machine gunner's head.

"The machine gunner was killed send out another!" Gramps ordered in Danish.

"Yes, sir!" the soldiers in the tank replied.

The tank cover or button as they call the door opened and like the scene in the movie *Saving Private Ryan* Alexi shot the first soldier right in the face. He held the cover open and Gramps then on the tank threw a couple of grenades down. Alexi dropped the cover and the duo jumped off the tank. As soon as their feet hit the ground the tank exploded with a thunderous boom. Alexi and Gramps cheered and laughed.

As the group moved out into the forests Gramps saw what Major Wolf had described so unapologetic and so candidly. Gramps remember how Wolf and other like Karl told him of such horrors they committed in Denmark and on the Eastern Front. The SS soldiers told it in great detail and were quite proud of it. Gramps now saw their work first hand. In the forest the bodies of men women, and children hung on the trees. Their bodies were frozen and looked black from various levels of decomposition exposed to the elements. Some of the bodies were missing limbs as the wildlife ate them. He looked in horror at these bodies and his eyes began to tear up. These were civilians and innocent people that were strung up. Some were as old as sixty and as young as four that were hung. He felt a surge of anger, hatred and sadness hit him all at once. He would like to say that it was better in the towns, villages, and cities that they went through but he would be lying. No, it was much worse and beyond anything that he had ever encountered up until then.

Some towns and cities that the group entered the civilians were hung from the street posts, and balconies thought the area. Most of the structures were reduced to rubble by explosives while others were still smoldering. In some areas it played out like that scene from the movie *The Patriot*. All of the townsfolk were corralled into the church where it was locked and lit on fire. More times than not everyone was killed as the Germans retreated. Although, the Soviet group would find a few survivors every so often that told them first-hand how everything unfolded. More times than not they would be suffering from shock of the trauma but still provided the bunch with some level of details.

When the Battle of Korson-Cherkassy Pocket was declared a Soviet victory on February 16th many of the Germans had escaped. However, in doing so they had left behind or were rather forced to abandon most of their supplies. The supplies included tanks, various small arms, millions of rounds of ammunitions, rations, uniforms, vehicles that included half-tracks, grenades and an assortment of explosives. The band of Red Army troops celebrated by cracking open a crate of German hooch. Gramps supposed he was caught up in the excitement or the alcohol but he grabbed Natalia by the wrist, spun her around, dipped her and kissed her for the very first time. He could tell that the Stalingrad veteran was quite surprised by it but nevertheless, she enjoyed it. As he brought her back upright they kissed again as she opened those beautiful blue eyes.

"Wow," Natalia whispered in Ukrainian and chuckled.

"I know," Gramps whispered softly in Russian.

Gramps and Natalia looked into each other's eyes for a moment and then they began smile and laugh. As he turned to see where Anna was he saw that she and Alexi were having a celebratory moment as well. Gramps and Nat just laughed and as they walked towards them then switch partners; Alexi had his arm around Natalia and Gramps had his around Anna. With their arms stretched around each other's shoulders they watched as the sun began to set upon their victory. It was later that Gramps learned that Natalia and Alexi were an item and before her the Soviet was with Anna. Alexi was a true ladies man and Gramps supposed that is why the men struck up a friendship as fast as they did.

As Gramps realized then watching that sun set with his new friends and lovers he couldn't help but think that there were some major surprises down the road but for now he didn't want to dwell on that. He just wanted to enjoy this moment as the sky turned a pinkish blue and wishing that it would never end. Although, he was back in love's tangled web he was very happy about it.

The engagement was known as the Battle of the Korsun-Cherkassy Pocket 24th January –16th February, 1944. It was part of the Dniper-Carpathian Offensive or more commonly known as the liberation of the right bank of Ukraine. In the offensive the Red Army fought the Germans in Ukraine, Poland, Moldova and Romania. The victory was just another step to the eventual liberation of Ukraine. The Soviets fought tooth and nail against the Germans to drive them out of the lands. It would be a long and bloody road with millions of civilians getting caught in the crossfire. However, it would be a while before the Red Army would have their vengeance as they march into the heart of Nazi Germany, Berlin and reduce the city to rubble.

As soon as I, now 13 years of age got home I went on the computer and plugged into Google Eastern Front World War II.

"Wow," I marveled.

I scrolled down the page and clicked on various websites. I read person accounts as well and overviews about the Soviet/German War. Some of the information was about the politics on both sides. A large chunk explained the personal hatred Joseph Stalin and Adolf Hitler had about one another. I clicked on videos of old men and I was blown away by them recanting their hellish experiences of the war.

Chapter 14

Anna

The group was put into reserve and they able to unwind for a month. Gramps learned how to speak Russian and Ukrainian at incredible lightning speed. He gave English lessons to Marko, Alexi, Natalia and Pidgin lessons to Anna. In the process of language lessons he learned much about his brothers and sisters in arms. For example Anna was just 16 when the Germans marched into her village and began to kill and rape everyone.

"My father gave my brothers his rifle and pistols that he had during the First World War. He then kissed me and my mother before he went outside to confront the Germans unarmed. It was the last time I ever saw him. A moment later we hear gunfire and a squad of SS troops stormed the house. My brothers killed one and wounded another before they were killed right in front of my mother and I. After my brothers were dead they raped my mother and then killed her with a bayonet. I was able to escape but rolled my ankle some time later. I was lucky I managed to ruin into a Soviet patrol who led me to their camp. I rested and once my ankle healed up I began to fight," Anna confessed to Gramps one night.

As Gramps held Anna in his arms under the stars, the only thing he could hear was the crackling of the fire and her sweet soft voice. He held her tighter and they kissed.

"So.. now I have told you my story what about yours?" Anna whispered softly.

"Well uh-" Gramps paused a moment to think about what to say. Gramps realized that Women were his weakness especially the last few. He also knew that there was a chance that Anna was a honeypot. A honeypot is a role in the spy world which is usually played by a women and her main goal is to seduce and sometimes turn their target. The goal or rather one of the honeypot's main ones is to get the target to open up and divulge information that they would not otherwise. The question was how willing he was to take that chance and tell the truth not part or half of it but the whole truth of himself? This one thought echoed loudly in his head as he made his decision. What seemed like an eternity of silence was in reality just mere minutes. Screw it; he went with mostly the truth.

And just like that he began to tell his story from milking cows and shooting birds with a BB gun just to steal watermelons from a patch back home. That night he told Anna everything from those tales to his time in the Philippines to his sabotage days with SOE in Denmark. He gave up everything except his orders to spy on the Soviets. Hell, he even told her tales of places and people that he had thought were lost in his mind forever. Anna she never once questioned any of it no, she just listened and took everything in. Anna had this thing about her that made him want to be open with her and well he guessed he felt for her. She broke him and that he supposed was it. He stared into her eyes as he recanted his life stories and just finished as the sun's rays broke upon the dark horizon. As the sun began to rise into the sky she kissed him and the couple kissed once more.

Anna was in fact an agent of the Main Intelligence Directorate, more commonly known as GRU, Soviet Military Intelligence. She was operating under the direct order of Joseph Stalin. Stalin had the idea that if Gramps couldn't be turned by a brother, then he was to be turned by a sister. He wanted the Japanese American to spill the wealth of intelligence on the inner workings of the Allies as well as the Axis he had been under. In Stalin's mind if he could play it right the hammer and sickle (the Soviet Flag) would wave beyond Europe and well into the Pacific and everywhere in between. At the very least he wanted to know a more pressing and urgent matter, how to wipe Hitler off. Anna's involvement as a part of Stalin's Secret Police was a closely held secret. She was such a monumental secret that it was not revealed until the collapse of the Soviet Union in 1991.

On one March morning Marko had given the group orders to move out and they hopped onboard the tanks as they sped out to engage the Germans. Their orders were simple surround and take out the Wehrmacht's 1st Panzer Army Group South. It sounded simple enough considering both the 1st and

2nd Ukrainian Fronts were going take them on. Over half a million Soviets in all went to take on the Panzer Army. Many of their tank divisions went before them and along with some ground troops. This earlier group cleared the way and dug in establishing defensive positions behind the German lines. If the Germans would attempt to break out they would be met with intense and heavy resistance.

On March 25 the German comms or communications were cut and nearly all of the Soviets took up positions surrounding the 1st Panzer Army in the city of Kamenets-Podolsky. The Germans were trapped inside a pocket in the city and now the Red Army was going to pour in from all sides to close the size of the gap. The Germans began to attempt to break out to the west. Two days later the vanguards or advance guard of the 1st Panzers headed toward the Zbruch River in the west. The front force managed to secure a few bridges while the back force or rearguard fought Soviet forces to cover the withdrawal. Meanwhile some of Grandpa's forces had driven deep into the pocket and was engaging the Southern portion of the Panzer Army. Red Army forces there had managed to kill most of the German defenders there and the rest retreated to rejoin their forces.

The commanders of the 1st and 2nd Ukrainian strongly believed that the Germans would attach from the South and ignored the engagements that came from the West. They believed it so much that they did nothing but beef up the forces attacking from the North and East. As Gramps and the group advanced on German position from the East and North they were met with very little resistance. In fact most of their positions were already abandoned as they withdrew to the city of Proskurov. Gramps was all ready to take on many Germans but nothing from the Northern portion. They engaged fewer than 50 enemy combatants and after they reported back to the higher ups.

The weather didn't help much with snow and frigid conditions. Gramps found out later that it was typical winter weather for Ukraine. The Germans managed to escape across the Strypa River on 5-6 April and hooked up with recon troops from some SS division close by to the town of Buczacz. After that he had no idea where the Germans went but they were celebrating another victory of sorts on the 15th. He meant they drove the enemy out but didn't kill them all like the previous battle. Nevertheless, it was a victory and they celebrated it in the usual fashion.

The Battle was called the Battle of Kamenets-Podolsky Pocket and ran from 25th March – 15th April. The battle is also known as Hube's Pocket named after the Commander of the 1st Panzer Army, General Hans-Valentin Hube. During the battle the Germans managed to escape the fate that their brothers in arms previously did not in Stalingrad and recently Korsun. They did so by anticipating Soviet tactics and constantly were on the move to avoid a freak out and getting wiped out. The tactics that the Germans used to escape is still being taught toady as a prime example of how to get out of a pocket without being completely destroyed.

Chapter 15

Celebrations

Once the celebrations were over the Soviet group went straight to the back and waited for the next engagement. In the reserve Marko showed off his book collection to Gramps. They were about 20 books all first editions and even a few of them were signed. The books were in a few languages including Russian, German, and English. Marko and Gramps talked with Anna by his side translating.

"Ah. I see why you want to learn English Comrade," Gramps said in English.

Anna translated and Marko chuckled.

"Do you like music?" Anna translated.

"Da," Gramps replied in Russian with interest.

Marko smiled and pulled out two Violins and an accordion. He then handed the Violins to Anna and Gramps. After that the Soviet Commander picked up the accordion and began to play Mozart's Requiem. It was quite interesting to hear with an accordion. Soon after others had heard the sweet sounds in the air they came investigate and joined in. Some brought out their Violins like Natalia and Alexi while others sang and made up the chorus. When that song was finished they all laughed and clapped. They then did other works by Mozart, Bach, Vivaldi, and finishing up with some Soviet Patriotic songs like their National Anthem as well as one of Grandpa's favorites Pachelbel's Canon. When their classical concert had finished Gramps could feel the atmosphere change. It was now lighter and warm as opposed to earlier being cold like he was still an outsider. Now, as he saw all those faces smiling and full of love it became apparent that he was now considered family. It felt that way more so than after his first victory with them. He wore the Soviet Uniform.

It was in that moment that Gramps felt right at home in the comfort of not strangers but family and lovers. People whom he would die for and now they would do the same for him. Music is truly the Universal language. You can be words apart from others and not even speak the same language but with music it doesn't matter. No, the beats of drums and the soft strokes of a Violin, that is truly universal.

"You still get one Violin?" I asked.

"Yeah. You like hear it?" Grandpa asked. He took a sip of his coffee.

"Hell yeah!" I exclaimed.

His face lit up in a mischievous grin.

"I'll be right back," he said and made a mad dash to his room.

After a couple of minutes, he came back out with a small case. The case looked like one you would store an ukulele in. It was shaped like a coffin and was made of wood. The case was painted back and was chipping as a sign of age. I ran my hand from one end to the other of the case. It was rough but still a bit smooth. My fingers curled onto the cold metal handle of the case. It was also smooth but pitted another sign of age. I opened it up and marveled at the wooden instrument.

"Wow," I whispered in awe.

"Yeah I said the same thing when I first saw it too. If you think this is somethin' just wait till you hear her. Man alive she sounds good!" He said.

He pulled the violin out and the bow from the case. He positioned the violin under his chin and began to strum using the bow. He was right the violin produced the sweetest sound I ever heard. For the next 20 minutes I sat there in awe as he played Canon in d and songs from Mozart. When he finished I said not a word still in awe of the antique instrument and the man who played it. I could see that he was sad after playing it.

"Grandpa how old is the violin?" I asked trying to cheer him up.

"Oh uh over 200," he said. He began to put her away in the case.

"What?" That is over 200 years old?" I shouted.

"Yeah this Stradivarius was made in 1723," he said plainly.

"Oh ok," I said. I took a sip of my can of root beer.

After he finished putting the violin back in the case he brought her back to his secret hiding spot.

"Now where we in the story?" he said after he emerged from his bedroom.

In the months that followed the Soviets opened up more to Gramps as did he to them. He taught them English and Pidgin English and they in turn taught him Russian and Ukrainian. They taught each other many things and shared stories of themselves. One day he was attempting to teach them how to play baseball, one of his favorite sports. Teaching them baseball was super funny to say the least. He explained that all those involved had many laughs in the process. While looking around he managed to find some lumber and with careful precision he carved a nice thick baseball bat. He had a baseball from home, so now he could teach.

Gramps demonstrated baseball with Anna faithfully by his side translating. Baseball 101, he called it and showed them to swing. The only problem was that in catching he didn't have any gloves so it became very apparent early on that this wasn't going to work. However, he managed to get the basics down over the course of four hours. One of the men hit the ball so far that it was lost and he called it quits then.

Gramps then rummaged in his bag and found a football. The football was flat and brand new so he rummaged around until he found a manual air pump. After he had pumped it up full he tossed it from hand. So, it was then that he decided to teach his next sport to the Soviets.

"Ok, now the objective is to keep the other team from scoring. Like in a firefight two people will cover the quarterback or the player with the ball on either side. You can take players out by tackling him or her to the ground. Also like battle you can have players deep in enemy territory and have the quarterback throw the ball to them to score if opposition is too heavy. When the player with the ball goes down and the ball touches the ground the game begins again where the player went down except the opposing team now has the ball," Anna translated Grandpa's instructions to Russian.

Many heads nodded in agreement and they broke up into two teams of ten. As the first play was under way it was quite funny and a bit hectic. Gramps had the ball with Anna and Alexi covering his right and left. Natalia who was on the opposite side with Marko covered the end zone as the duo kicked, flipped and pummeled any opposing players who dared to venture that deep. Gramps was surprisingly taken back by how strong Natalia was as she took out men that had height as well as weight over her. As he mentioned before both Natalia and Anna were extremely physically fit and had abs as well as muscles on their arms and legs. They didn't look like the ripped female body builders of today but make no mistake they had muscles.

Gramps was nearly by Marko when wham out of nowhere Peter took out both he and Anna. The three of them were kissing the dirt. When he went down Gramps hit the ground so hard he was now seeing stars in broad daylight! As the game resumed they began to laugh as they tackled other to the ground. Natalia ended up scoring with Marko and Andrei protecting her right and left flanks. After an intense two hours of playing and many bruises later Grandpa's team won by one point. As the group regardless of what side they played on extended a hand and helped on another get back on our feet. They patted each other on the back and praised how they all played. They drank vodka and toasted to playing two new sports and to numb out physical aches and pains as a result of it.

Alexi pulled out a battered pair of boxing gloves and showed them to Gramps. He had a flashback to a teacher he had long ago. The male teacher had a pair of boxing gloves that he maintained which hung in plain view on the wall behind his desk. Whenever kids would disrespect him he would say 'put on the glove' and they would put on the gloves. However the teacher had two secrets that he was an amateur boxer and he had a long arm. His advantage of a long arm was that the kid could swing all he wanted but he would hold them at an arm length away. Usually the kid would swing until he came tired and the teacher would let him go. The only difference on the Eastern Front was that Alexi and the other guy would gear up with one side glove and really pummel each other.

The group split into squads of 12 and as long range scouts ventured deep behind German lines. They gathered intelligence on troop movements, size of force and type of equipment. On surprise the Soviets would take them head on Rambo style or one man army and shoot them up. Most times however, the Germans outnumbered them by a lot so as much as they wanted to strike they had to restrain themselves not to. The Soviets much like the Japanese didn't care if they were outnumbered they were going to strike and that was it. Their mentality was that they didn't care if they were gonna die in the process of attacking the enemy they just saw it as taking down as many of the enemy they could before they went down themselves.

They smiled at death like an old friend. If they fall in battle so be it in their eyes especially the Japanese there is no greater honor that of one to die in battle. This was something that the Americans and the British could never understand. The Soviets were thirsty for revenge and they were going to let it loose on every German and every collaborator regardless.

One June morning Gramps awoke to the sound of celebration, he went out of the hut to see what was going on.

"What is it?" Gramps asked Anna very groggy.

"The Americans in combined forces attacked Normandy, France," Anna replied excited.

"What?" He asked dumbfounded.

"The Americans are now fighting the Nazis in Western Europe," she said unable to contain her excitement.

Gramps began to cheer and laugh. The Americans were now in Hitler's Fortress Europe and he couldn't be happier. Nearly everyone got extremely drunk over the news and it was clear that they now had a good chance of winning the war.

On June 6, 1944 the Allies launched a massive operation codenamed Operation Overlord. The target was Normandy, France. Thousands of British, American, and Canadian troops would be part of the operation. The invasion of Normandy was a land, sea and air assault. Due to a blunder of sorts paratroopers from three countries landed all over Southern France instead of their targeted drop zones. By sea and air the beaches were bombarded by heavy fire but for the well dug in Germans they remained untouched and safe in their underground bunkers. Landing crafts filled with soldiers descended onto the beaches. There were five codename beaches all together with the Americans at Utah and Omaha, the British with Gold and Sword and the Canadians with Juno. The battle was a bloodbath for both the Allies and Germans but would be a victory for the Allies.

In July the group was called to the front and once again thrown into the fire. On July 13 they nailed the Germans and easily took a town. By nightfall they had broken through the German lines and were deep inside. On the next day Soviet planes roared in the skies as they let loose bullets and bombs on the Germans. Mortars whistled down on the Soviets and exploded. MG-42s spat rounds everywhere and implanting themselves into

Grandpa's Soviet buddies. It was total chaos and yet it was only just the beginning.

"Natalia! Take out the Mortar crew!" Gramps yelled in Ukrainian.

Natalia nodded and went to take up a position.

Natalia was equipped with a scoped rifle and boy the girl was artist with it! As the mortars continued to rain down upon them Peter, Alexi, Anna and several others attempted to take out the MGs that were cutting down their men. Gramps gave them covering fire and distracted the German gunners as they flanked them. They managed to take out two MG-42 positions and countless infantrymen. Natalia climbed up on the remains of a building and from the vantage point she took out the mortar crews. Gramps watched with binoculars as she gave the thumbs up after she took out the last mortar crew. Three of their tanks steamrolled their path and they emerged from behind the tank guns blazing on the German infantry.

The group paved the way and wiped out the Germans in their path. As they advanced Soviet planes roared overhead as they strafed the enemy on the ground below. All of a sudden German artillery began to rain down and destroyed one of the Soviet tanks.

"Artillery! Take cover!" Alexi yelled in Russian.

Men who were riding on the tanks hastily jumped off and joined units on the ground. Four Panzer tanks peaked behind some buildings and suddenly came to life as the group of Soviets passed them. Gramps saw the main gun turret swivel; his eyes became wide and he grabbed Anna. The couple went down the ground just as the Panzer fired and shook the building it had been hidden behind. As Gramps used his body and shielded Anna, Alexi did the same with Natalia. Peter and two others went to place explosives on the tanks while the rest of them tried not to get killed being the distraction for them. Once the set the explosives on the tanks there was a 30 second timer on them. The tanks went up in thunderous booms just a few seconds apart from each other. Large clouds of black smoke danced from the now out of commission Panzers.

As the group progressed deeper into German held territory they fought in cities and through its streets. They stormed buildings in an effort to locate and destroy their enemy. They located weapon stockpiles and gained creditable intelligence from German POWs as they interrogated them on the spot. Gramps was among the interrogators because of his intimate knowledge of the German Armed Forces as well as language fluency. Gramps wasn't as insane as Marko but he did pull his pistol and threaten to shoot their nuts off. The threat usually worked because no man wants to be shot in the balls. Hell, even fanatical SS men broke down upon the threat. Gramps supposed they saw that he was crazier than them and he had this glare in his eyes which he guessed worked. Looking back on those moments if they had tested him he would have fired in their nuts. Yes, he was that hell bent and the seven long months began to change him to a – Soviet.

The intense fighting went on until the end of August when it was declared a Soviet Victory. They were exhausted from fighting and then the order came down that the Soviets had won. They were in Poland at the time and they were all ecstatic about the win but greatly tired and looked forward to some time off in the reserve. Gramps looked back with the sun in his face and though for a moment how far all of them had come. Gramps, in particular just seven months ago parachuted to a group of strangers and now they were brothers, sisters, and lovers. They had liberated Ukraine and now were battling the Germans out of Poland.

"My god had it really been that long. Seven frickin' months," Gramps thought to himself.

Gramps had fought in the hellish winter of the Eastern Front, in and near the Carpathian Mountains, in villages, towns and cities. He now was considered a fellow brother in the Soviet Army and was in Poland celebrating his third victory. As the reality of his journey began to sink in he had to step back a moment. Never had he thought he would be right here, right now but he was and that to him was something.

The air was filled with smoke and death. It was such a distance to home which was such a foreign concept for Gramps. He hadn't been home in over two years and didn't think about it as much as before. It now seemed to be a distant memory or that thing on the tip of your tongue. He could recall memories of himself fishing and others but now they seemed to be of someone else and not him. As he realized that it was indeed the same person his fear began to set in. How was he going to explain to his family what he had seen and done? All the horrors and atrocities as well as the happiness and joy. It was the first time he had really taken the time to think about it and it terrified the hell out of him. Although, it was only on the condition that he would make it back to Kauai alive and in one piece. For though they were winning the war was not over yet and it was still a long way to Berlin. After all they were only in Poland and they still had not yet touched German soil.

The battle was called the Lvov-Sandomierz Offensive which ran from July 13 – August 29. It was fought in Western Ukraine and Easter Poland. In the fighting the mighty German Army was pushed farther back than ever before. Poland was the first battle of the Second World War in 1939 and was the first country to fall by force. In doing so the Soviets were able to capture key bridges and thus gained a stronghold in Romania. It was heavy fighting but eventually the Germans folded and retreated. It was another step to the path to Berlin, the heartland of Germany.

Chapter 16

New Companions

Around this time Gramps got to know the men and women better. As his language skills in Russian and Ukrainian became fluent he could communicate much better with everyone. They were in small skirmishes with the Germans but nothing too heavy. He found out that Marko and Alexi had another brother Gregory who died in the Battle of Kiev back in 1941. The brother was the middle child. The death of their brother only fueled their thirst to kill every Nazi they could find. Marko was the more brutal one where as Alexi preferred to kill them straight out rather than torture.

One night Marko told a Russian joke and Gramps didn't recall how it went but he knew he was the only one who didn't get it. He tried telling local Hawaii jokes but they never got it. He taught many of them or tried to anyway English and Pidgin English. The girls took well as did Alexi and Marko. Others took somewhat but needed more time to get the pronunciations right on the mark. He was amazed at how Natalia and Anna were able to hit the pronunciations of Pidgin words right on the money. Marko did well in English but not so much in Pidgin whereas Alexi was the exact opposite.

As summer began to change to fall the dreaded chill of winter began to blow. Alexi, Natalia, Anna and Gramps would go on walks and hikes. There they would marvel at the animals they would encounter like birds, squirrels, wolves and others. It was here in the Carpathian Mountains that they stumbled upon four wolf pups. The mother had been bled out from a rifle round to her side and was dead for a couple of days. They heard the cries of the pups in the distance and followed it. They ended up off the trail and after nearly half an hour of walking through trees they ended up by a cave on the side of a mountain. The wolf pups were these cute, small gray things. They didn't think the pups would survive and were amazed that they had as long as they did.

In that littler of four there was one boy and three girls. Anna, Natalia and Gramps took the three girls while Alexi took the single boy. They took them to camp and showed them to the others. Their fellow comrades all agreed that the pups were cute and beautiful. In the weeks after they nursed them back to health and racked their heads at the perfect names for their cuddly new friends. After much deliberation Gramps decided on the name Ka'iulani after the last Princess of the Hawaiian Monarchy. It was also decided by Marko that their wolves be trained in different languages unique to the owner so that the Germans couldn't stop them. The four troops were also instructed to teach one other person the language in which they trained their wolves should the owner perish in combat. So, Gramps decided to train Ka'iulani in Hawaiian and picked Anna to teach.

For her wolf Anna picked the name Maria and decided that she was going to train the wolf in Pig Latin. Anna picked Gramps as the one to teach Pig Latin to. In asking about the name she picked for her wolf Gramps found out the origin of her own name. Anna was short for Anastasia as in the last Grand Duchess of Russia. Anna was not the Russian Princess but simply had been named after her. Alexi named his Henry Morgan or HM for short. He named the wolf after his idol the 17th Century Pirate Henry Morgan. He loved the tales of the Pirates of old and collected many books on them. He often talked about settling down in Jamaica and living the quiet life after the war was over. He trained HM in Spanish and taught it to Natalia. Natalia named her Emilia and taught it Greek. She chose the name and the language because before the war her family had a dog with the same name. Natalia loved the stories and myths of Ancient Greece and dreamed about living there after the war. She taught Greek to Alexi who took it with some difficulty at first then quickly got it.

One day Gramps was called to the radio tent and his whole world was turned upside down. He walked into the tent, his girl and his buddies all waited there with grim looks on their faces.

"This is Dragon 577 over," Gramps said over the radio.

"We read you Dragon 577 We have some bad news son. Your father has died. Over," the male voice in a British accent said.

"Wh- wha- What did he die if-if you know. Over," Gramps stammered in shock.

"Heart attack, over." The voice replied.

"Thank you for letting me know. Over," Gramps replied.

"You're welcome and sorry for your loss. Over," the voice said.

As nothing but static came through the radio Gramps just stood there frozen of shock. His father was dead and he was half a world away.

"I am so sorry Ken," Anna said. She gave Gramps a big hug.

The next few days are still a blur to Gramps but he did remember many soldiers expressing their condolences to him. Memories of him and his Father began to flood him and Gramps was immensely overwhelmed by it. Home seemed like such a lifetime ago and well it was a reminder that it wasn't. One night he broke down sobbing and Anna comforted him. It was in that moment Gramps knew that she truly cared for him. Anna realized she was unable to fulfil her secret duty. She sent a long coded message to Stalin regarding this via Morris Code. She received no reply back.

When the group saw heavy action again it was January 1945 and in the dead of another hellish winter. As the chilled breeze hit Grandpa's skin it felt like he was being stabbed by a blade. By this time it was pretty clear that the war was nearly over. Although to the die-hard Nazis they were still winning and the losses were just setbacks. The Germans in defeat and retreat in both Eastern and Western Europe. The fighting was still pretty intense and both sides refusing to lighten up. As they fought in the streets they go into some heavy firefights. In some cases ambushes with small arms and shoulder fired rockets.

When the group searched a building they first threw a couple of grenades in the window on the bottom floor. Immediately after it exploded 15 of them went in to search it floor by floor. They anxiously searched the building room by room and to their surprise they only encountered light resistance. Once the all clear was given they counted and collected the dead bodies of the enemy. They counted 22 dead Wehrmacht in all and it was off to the next building.

As the group walked in the streets it was quiet and that made them all feel uneasy. As soon as they turned a corner two MG-42s opened up. They were on the rooftops of two buildings on the right and left. They were now caught in deadly crossfire right out in the open. They all dove back behind the corner and started to deliberate on how they were going to get out of this mess.

"Ken do you still have that Panzerschreck?!" Marko yelled in Russian between the gunfire.

"Yeah. Peter! GET OVER HERE!" Gramps yelled in Russian.

The plan was that the rest of them would distract both enemy machine guns while Peter took aim and fired at one. The shot from the German bazooka was a direct hit and the enemy gun position exploded brightly. Then, all of a sudden German soldiers poured out of the building up the street. The Red Army troops emerged from their cover and a massive firefight ensued. Anna and Gramps covered Peter while he got into position to take out the last MG nest. The Russian fired and it was another spectacular explosion as a result of a direct hit.

The fighting on the ground intensified so much that it became hand to hand combat. Knives, blades, fists, helmets and whatever you could imagine were now being used to take out one another. Gramps on the other hand decided to use his martial art skills and Samurai sword to take them out. He used a variety of slashes, blocks, kicks, punches, palms and anything else you could think of to kill the Germans. Once the battle was over there was no celebration instead it was off to the next engagement.

It was in the next battle where Natalia and Gramps were assigned by Marko to go on a long range recon mission.

On their recon mission the pair met very heavy resistance and they did more than once get German attack dogs on them. The Ukrainian and American had no choice but to retreat and after three days on the run with limited sleep they were greatly confused and lost. At least they weren't alone besides the two of them they also had their wolves to keep them company. What a help the wolves were because in addition to alerting them on enemies they also kept natural predators away. The pair's four legged friends were skilled hunters but even they seemed to have a hard time finding food in the harsh winter. It was early on the morning of the fifth day that a Soviet patrol ran into them. The wolves growled and naturally when the patrol found them, all the troops had their guns drawn with their fingers on the triggers at the ready. It was an extremely tense moment with

Ka'iulani and Emilia barking, growling, and showing their razor sharp chompers with the drool oozing out of their mouths.

"Who are you?" the Soviet SGT asked in Ukrainian with his weapon still trained on them.

"We are Lieutenant Natalia and Major Ken of the 13th Army," Natalia stated.

The Sarge eyed Gramps for a moment and then slowly lowered his weapon. He shouted a command and the rest of the unit lowered their weapons. Gramps knew despite all the dirt and grime on his face that their interest was peaked because of him being Japanese.

The recon unit who were all enisled men nodded to the duo but dared not to salute them in case of enemy snipers in the area. Natalia and Gramps were due to be promoted but because it was a slow process they didn't know if it had gone through yet. The unit identified themselves as Privates and a Sarge of the 322nd Rifle Division, 60th Army. Both of them were part of the 1st Ukrainian Front and glad to have still run into their guys. However, after they were taken back to the unit's lines they had no idea that they were off as much as they were.

The unit took the pair to a tent which had a small table and a map which sat on top of it. There was one high ranking officers, a Colonel. The Colonel was the CO (commanding officer), he simply sat slumped in a chair and clutched a large bottle of vodka which was nearly gone.

"Colonel we have company, sir." The Sarge informed in Russian.

The Colonel turned slowly and waved the men off. The men nodded, clicked their heels and left. Once the pair was alone the Colonel got up and spoke to them. He stated his name but for the life of him Gramps couldn't seem to recall it.

"I would like access to a radio to inform our CO that we are all right," Gramps stated in Russian.

"Very well I will have one brought here in a moment. Drink?" the Colonel asked. He grabbed an unopened large bottle of Vodka from a crate.

"Sure," Natalia answered with a smile.

After they each took sips from the bottle they got down to business.

"We really need to get back to our lines Colonel," Gramps said. He stressed.

"I am sorry Major but I cannot allow it. For you see we have loss many men in particular officers. We cannot spare anymore of them," he explained. He twisted the ends of his mustache.

Just then a Private came in with a radio and set it up. Once he finished he nodded to them and left.

Gramps looked at Natalia and saw her answer in her eyes. Gramps nodded at her then looked back at the Colonel.

"All right Colonel we will stay until this offensive is over. Then we will return to our outfit," Gramps stated.

He nodded.

"Thank you Major and Captain. I will leave you to your call," he said. He got up from his chair.

As he walked to the opening of the tent he stop dead in his tracks and spun back around to face them.

"By the way Major Ken you are an odd one are you not?" he remarked.

"Do explain," Gramps said. Natalia played with the dial on the radio.

"Well you are Japanese are you not?" he stated.

"Yes. I am-adopted," Gramps said with a straight face.

"Ah I see. Well if you need me I will be at mess," he said.

He then nodded and left.

Quite a bit of static hissed from the radio but after 20 minutes of fidgeting, Natalia zeroed in on their unit's frequency and got ahold of Marko. She explained to him what had happened and although he didn't like it he was relieved to hear from them. After the pair finished up the talk with Marko they went out of the tent and were shown their quarters by the Colonel. The pair had a nice large tent and because Natalia was a woman it was just for the two of them. The Colonel appeared desperate to make them comfortable as possible. Just by taking a look around the camp and seeing the dead, the wounded and how little number of able bodies he had they were grateful for these accommodations. They ate horse soup (yes Gramps did say horse in case you seemed to be imagining it) and although it tasted a bit off from possibly being old, it was not the worst thing he ate. The monkey he ate in the Philippines was – well he did say monkey didn't he, so let's leave it at that.

As darkness fell Natalia and Gramps slept on opposite sides of the tent. However, at some point late in the night or early in the morning she snuggled up with him. He was, according to her half-awake when she did. She didn't want to be alone so curled up next to him at least that's how she recanted the tale to him later the next morning. He had feelings for her he will not lie but after those romantics went away it was like a best friend / brother relationship that they had. The romantics he had felt early on when they had met but those faded away to what relationship they had now.

Chapter 17

The Horrors of War

Gramps and Natalia fought and led with great success winning battle after battle with their new men. They gained much ground and with minimum casualties on their end. By the end of January they were flying in high spirits. However, the discovery of one of the most infamous Nazi Death Camps was about to derail it all. On January 27, 1945 Soviet forces discovered and set foot in Auschwitz Death Camp. Gramps had gotten into an argument with another solider and who blindsided him with the butt of a rifle which rendered him unconscious. When Gramps came to he was being given a big kiss on the lips by what looked like to him at the time an obake (ghost). When Gramps woke up more he realized that it was a middle aged man who stood around his height. The man looked like a walking skeleton with all the bones of his body clearly visible. He was speaking Polish which Gramps didn't understand and continued to smile, scream in delight, hug and kiss him.

Then all of a sudden the reality began to sink into the man and he began to weep. Gramps held this man who was only skin and bones in his arms as a river of tears began to flow onto his shoulder. Gramps began to comfort him in Danish which to his upmost surprise he then spoke back to the Japanese American in and thus the language barrier was broken. His name was Adam, a businessman and he described the unspeakable horrors that occurred at the camp.

"The Germans separated families, one member goes to this train and the others go to another. We were taken like cattle and packed into trains as such. We were treated worse than dirt and when we arrived at the camp it was much worse. Slave labor, starvation, physical and mental torture, various wide spread diseases and the threat of the gas chamber was what we lived and perished under," Adam reveled in Danish.

Other Soviet troops went door to door and pulled out thousands of people who were nothing but walking skeletons. Their living conditions were beyond horrible. The stench of rotting bodies combined with the horrid smell burning flesh made even those who had ironclad stomachs churn. As the search continued some soldiers found rooms with large industrial ovens with human remains inside still burning. As Red Army soldiers continued their search others tried to find out what happened here. According to one of the Men, Natalia talked with said that when they got word of the Soviets coming they tried to kill as many of the captives as possible before running out to save themselves. This is supported by Adam and the fact that those ovens were still on when the group came marching in.

The group found that many if not all of these people who were imprisoned here were Jewish. That was their only so called crime being Jewish. The Nazis viewed Jews as a race rather than a religion and thus killed millions on this belief. However, in Grandpa's opinion the Jews were not a race but a religion. He meant every nationality has them so it only makes sense that way. The medics checked out all of the newly liberated people and all instructed the troops to not feed them heavily because at the state they are in their bodies can't handle a large amount of food. So, the rescuers fed the Jewish civilians little bit and some out of habit began to hide the food in their pockets. Later the Jewish folks were loaded onto transports where they were driven to safe havens behind Soviet lines for some much needed rest and proper medical care.

The group came across a large train with many closed train cars. The closer they got to the train cars the louder a unison buzzing sound became. At first it sounded like hives of buzzing bees but when the Soviet troops opened the cars it revealed something much worse. The first thing that hit was the horrible view of dozens of heavily decomposing bodies. The second was the strong awful stench that once was in the nose was impossible to get out. The third was the millions of flies all over the bodies and in the air. It looked like a black swarm.

The liberators also found some of their fellow Soviets among the Jews. The soviets were troops that had been captured in various battles since the

German/Soviet War began in 1941. Like the Jews, they too spoke of nightmarish horrors that were inflicted upon them. Many were extremely eager to repay the Germans with the same treatment but they were physically far too weak. They could hardly walk but still wanted to fight. "Comrades, I know you wish to fight those evil fuckers. So, rest, become strong and live. For they tried to kill you, all of you. For life is the greatest revenge you can inflict upon them. Leve the killing to your fellow brothers and sisters. I promise we will make them feel the rest," the Colonel declared.

Everyone joyfully cheered.

After the group said their goodbyes and farewells they marched on to find those responsible and kill them. After that camp they were given orders not to take prisoners but to kill ever last one.

As the group of Soviets moved out their feelings changed if there was even a sliver of compassion towards the German troops it was gone. Replaced by a deep hatred and a burning desire to kill them all not only for the unspeakable crimes they have done to the Russian people but to all those Jewish people in the camps as well. They came to a halt in early February and thus the offensive was over so Gramps and Nat returned to their outfit.

I got to hear first hand the horrors Grandpa witnessed at the National Holocaust Museum in Washington D.C. in March 2012. I and fellow classmates of my high school went there as part of school trip. They couldn't wait to get out of there while I was at home surrounded with all that history. I got separated as usual from my peers and jumped into a led tour. The tour was being led by a survivor of this infamous act in history.

We saw the trains with the doors open and the mountain of shoes.

When the group got to the train the guide an elderly white woman stopped.

"Now, this train and cars were filled with shoes. But, there was one that Soviet forces reportedly found something very different. They noted a very loud buzzing sound, like that of a hive of bees. Upon opening the car doors they were horrified that it-"

"Was a swarm of a million flies," I finished.

The elderly lady nodded.

The room and group was silent as they were absorbing the words that was said.

After a moment of pure silence and very somber looks the lady talked once more.

"How did you know it was flies and not bees?" She asked. She looked at me closely.

I looked directly at her and began.

"My Grandfather was part of the 1st Ukrainian Front. He told me the sight was like a biblical plague. Some of the troops began to anoint themselves in a cross. Others began to say prayers. It was a cold January day in 1945. The camp's name was Auschwitz," I revealed. I never broke eye contact.

I now broke contact and saw the entire led group of a dozen with their eyes and faces in complete and utter disbelief. The room was dead silent. After the full grown adults had absorbed all the words they went one by one shaking my hand and thanking my Grandfather. They called him a hero. It was the very first time I had ever heard anyone call Gramps a hero other than me. I was very taken back by it.

When they got back Alexi and Anna had many questions for them however, none more that Marko. The pair got the official word that they were now promoted to Major and Lieutenant. They had many stories to tell but first Marko wanted to find out all of those whom they had been in contact with. Gramps guessed with his background Marko had to do some damage control to insure that Gramps was a well-guarded secret. After all it's not the greatest thing for tales of Japanese man in a Soviet uniform roaming around Europe fighting the Germans. So, after that talk they had their celebratory drink and well- you know what else.

After the offensive had ended the reunited group was at the Oder River 43 miles away from Berlin. The offensive was known as the Vistula-Oder Offensive. It got the name from the two rivers that it began and ended at. The offensive ran from January 12- February 2, 1945 and took Soviet forces from Central Poland to Eastern Germany within 43 miles of Berlin the Capital city of Germany. The big wig Generals halted their forces at the Oder River thus ending the offensive. However, that didn't really sit well with the troops because here was the crown jewel and heart of Germany less than 50 miles away from the troops and they couldn't just march in now.

Shit! Gramps meant it's like they were teasing them or some shit!

In not letting Soviet forces pass the river and nail Berlin in February gave the Germans time to prepare and regroup in anticipation of the Red Army's arrival. Most of the forces that the Soviets seemed to encounter now were of old men and young kids. It still amazed Gramps that they literally killed and or captured nearly an entire Generation.

By now food had become very scarce and so they "liberated" everything and ate anything. Horses, pigs, foxes, you name it chances are they had at least once. The group heard that some troops turned to their German POWs and consumed them. Although, thankfully they didn't have to resort to those extremes. Personally, Gramps was not quite sure what he would have done if they did have to. For Gramps thought of having to be a cannibal to survive seemed so extreme but it was a possibility and for some a reality.

The group were constantly busy for there were many pockets of resistance and so they fought with great fury to take them out. In addition to Soviet and captured German hardware they also had American as well. Yep, Sherman tanks, Harley Davidson and Indian bikes as well as an assortment of weapons and other things made in the good ole U.S. of A! The reason that had this stuff as well as the British was because of the Lend-Lease Program. President Roosevelt signed it in September 1940 before the U.S. got into the war and as a result many allies who were already at war with Japan and Germany received U.S. made supplies.

However, because the Soviet Union had signed a pact with the Germans were not part of the bill. It was only after they were attacked by the Germans did they get on the bill too. They signed on in June 1941 and the first batch of supplies arrived four months later. Gramps had a laugh when he saw U.S. made Sherman tanks being driven by Soviets there. Hell he even had a laugh when he saw Harley Davidson and Indian motorcycles in London, England! Seeing these things so far from home made him laugh but they also made him think of home and how far he was as well. It made him a bit sad and afraid that the longer he was away the less he remembered of home. It seemed like a lifetime ago he was fishing on the shore and prying Opihi off the rocks. He could hardly remember what it was like to not have to worry about anything. He shuddered to think about the product this war had made of him. He quickly got rid of these thought because if he didn't they surely would be the end of him.

By the time the group cleared the German pockets they realized the war was lost for them. So, as a result they began to get desperate. In doing this it resulted in two things the Germans either went erratic and tried to kill as many Soviet troops as they could or they immediately threw down their weapons and surrendered right on the spot. No matter what they decided to do the troops of the Red Army won anyway because many of the Soviets wanted to kill every single one who donned that uniform. It depended on who the Germans surrender as if they wound be spared or be tortured and or killed on the spot.

The lucky Germans that they did take as prisoners were interrogated by Petrov a Sarge who was not a guy you wanted to bump into at night. He had a thick mustache, was quite buff and had a spooky looking face. He was a sadist who like Marko had great pleasure in torturing others. Gramps supposed that is why Marko liked the fellow Russian so much because they were alike. You could hear the screams through the day and night. Dozens of German POWs met their deaths at the hands of Petrov. The Russians were out for blood pure and simple, in a way Gramps could relate he was pissed at the Japanese for attacking his home. He was also angry at the Americans for how they treated the Japanese Americans and Japanese immigrants who have lived in the U.S. for many years. Putting his anger in fighting against the Germans worked however, in war no one wins.

After the pockets cooled off some of their men transferred over to other units and were part of the Silesian Offensives. The offensives were in two parts the Lower Offensive which ran from February 8-24 and the Upper Offensive March 15-31. The Lower offensive paved the way for troops to the city of Breslau. The Siege of Breslau ran from February 13- May 6 and due to the destruction that both sides inflicted the nearly the entire city was obliterated.

Some of their men mainly tanks and their crews had just gotten back from fierce fighting in the Battle of Seelow Heights. The battle which ran from April 16-19 was part of the last phases of the encirclement of Berlin. As the group got into position along with thousands of other Soviets they asked one another what they planned to do after the war. With Berlin in their sight they set out to the capital city of Nazi Germany a feat that seemed impossible just months earlier.

"What you got planned Alexi?" Gramps asked. He turned to Alexi.

"I don't know brah," Alexi answered. He shrugged his shoulders.

That answer seemed to be all of them because not a single person had expected to live to see the war end. They all had thought about it at one time or another but their years of combat in addition to what they endured had simply changed them. The group shared a special bond uniquely only to those who had seen action. The kill or be killed mentality was something so much a part of them it would remain instilled for the rest of their born days. Like it or not the war had made them into all killers and savages as well as masters in the art of modern warfare. All of them whether they wanted to admit it or not realized in that moment that they would have to face what they had become. They all came to terms with that in their own way. Some learned to lock it up somewhere while others found solace at the bottom of a bottle of 120 proof vodka. However of the many ways they chose and sometimes those choices led them down even darker paths. I'm getting a bit ahead of myself again so let's get back to the story. Where were they? As, yes just outside of Berlin.

Part of the 1st Ukrainian Front was to begin attacking from the South in a place called Halbe while part 1st Belorussian Front attacked from the North creating a pocket of trapped Germans. This was closing the gaps between Soviet forces and Berlin. On April 23 other parts of both moved into position, encircling Berlin. There was extremely heavy artillery covering fire for them courtesy of the 1st Belorussian Front. The artillery fire began in April 20 and didn't cease until the Hiterites surrendered. Scores of Soviet fighters and bombers dominated the skies. They conducted numerous strafing and bombing runs.

Remembering Grandpa's stories the words swirled around me as I found myself entrenched in my first fight ever. It was in my middle school years and the kid was same grade as me. He was a skinny Caucasian with staggering basketball height of over six feet with long arms. Harsh words were exchanged and it ended with food and drink beings spilled, or at least I thought it ended. About an hour after the spills we were in the locker room and the guy pissed off lunged at me. At that time, I still used rolling backpacks and so I grabbed it and tried to swing it in his face but he grabbed it and tore it out of my hands like Willie Wonka's last golden ticket. I fell backwards and that's all I remember. I didn't get knocked out from the fall but I just don't remember what happened after that. All I know is something else happened after that and the fight was over.

The war was reaching its grand finale and with the close ushering a new era to the world as they picked up the pieces. The group all were eager to get into Berlin and end this world war once and for all. As they reached the outskirts of the city they were greeted with many empty houses and fresh corpses. The stench of corpses in the early stages of decomposition was an all too familiar smell to the veteran soldiers by now. Like in many other areas they encountered in Germany families including young children had committed suicide prior to their arrival. They would rather die by their own hands than be under Soviet rule. Gramps didn't blame them but to see the lifeless bodies of young children simply undid him. He could not blame the parents for killing their own kids because he knew what the Russians would have done to them all of them. It was the sad truth of war one that he would carry for the rest of his life.

The group got into closer positions and anxiously waited to storm the city, guns blazing. The U.S. relentlessly bombed Berlin during the day and the British did runs at night. On April 24 just after several barrages of Soviet rockets called Katyusha or better known as Stalin's Organs they stormed the city on a captured Hiterite Tiger tank. They yelled as they went in and on all sides of the tank soldiers rushed in before them. Behind their tank they shielded some of their men two of whom were armed with flamethrowers. Blown out buildings still smoldered and some still on fire. Glass and rubble were everywhere. Gunfire erupted and many incoming rounds ricocheted off the heavily armored tank.

"Yuri! Torch the room!" Natalia hissed.

"Covering fire!" Alexi yelled and fired.

Yuri under the cover of several of them broke formation and with three other soldiers behind him let his flamethrower loose on a café. After a few seconds German troops on fire ran out of the café screaming.

"Do not fire! Let the bastards cook!" Gramps yelled in Russian. Many of the soldiers aim their weapons on the burning Germans.

The troops nodded and continued to pick off other German troops around them. As they breached the city scattered sniper fire ripped all over. Gramps fell off the tanks and joined up with Anna and the rest of the men on the ground.

"Are you all right Ken?" Anna asked as she helped him to his feet.

"Yeah. Just a bit dazed," Gramps replied. He brushed himself off.

Just then the unmistakable rumble of two tiger tanks from the left was heard and they opened fire with their main gun. In a thunderous boom two solid building crumbled and in the smoke the enemy tanks fired once more. Peter and a couple others buttoned up and charged head first to engage the tank. With their cover gone German troops seized the chance and charged at them in full force with guns blazing. Gramps along with Alexi sprayed the charging Germans with their burp guns (PPSH M1941) as a dozen Red Army troops darted for cover in the building to the right.

"Alexi! Pop smoke!" Gramps yelled between the heavy gunfire.

Alexi nodded and pulled out two smoke grenades. He pulled the pins off and threw them. As they dispersed smoke and with visibility low they too made their way to the building. From there they began the task of clearing the building. It had three floors and a basement plenty of places for the Germans to ambush them. As four of the men slowly walked up the stairs and three watched their backs ready to take out any Germans from the door and windows. The rest of them took aim at the top and waited for the enemy to pop up.

"Help us! The Lieutenant has been shot!" Gramps yelled in German.

Then they saw three German troops slowly emerge from the hall. The men up top gave them rifle butts to their stomach and slid their throats. Silent kills were key in not giving the enemy the slip the party crashers were here.

"Is everything all right there Josef?" a voice called out in German from the top floor.

"Yes, sir," Gramps replied back in German. He looked at Alexi.

"Good. How is the view from there? the voice asked.

"Shit! Get ready! Gramps whispered in Russian. He looked at his squad.

"Uh- it is clear," Gramps nervously answered in German.

Right after that response the place erupted with gunfire and German yells. Bullets went flying all over the place. They ran up the stairs and were met face to face with 20 Germans and fire from an MG-42 situated up on the top floor. One of their guys emptied a mag in three Germans. He was hit in the shoulder with a rifle round. Anna sprayed the hallway as Alexi unloaded on the MG nest. They once again dove for cover and smashed through the door on the left. They surprised four Germans in the room and Gramps took them out with his revolver before they could grab their weapons.

As they were being engaged from enemy troops from the hall and the room on the right a mortar round exploded right on the street outside.

"Is that ours?" Gramps asked. He turned to Alexi.

He nodded slowly with a large grin on his face.

"Great I came all this way only to die by friendly fuckin' fire!" Gramps muttered in English.

As the mortars rained down on the group's position the walls suddenly erupted with bullets. Gramps threw a grenade into the room on the right, taking out the enemies in there. They fired at the walls and Gramps gave covering fire by the door as the others sneaked behind him to the room on the right. Gramps emptied mag after mag and soon ran out. He dropped the burp gun and picked up an STG-44 from a dead German. He plucked the extra mags from the dead body with bullets whizzing over his head. As he darted to the door a stick grenade landed by his foot, he kicked it towards the Germans in front of him and frantically dove into the room.

The Germans screamed as the grenade exploded and splinters from the wooden floors and walls flew. As the group slowly got up with their ears ringing Gramps looked across and slow motion saw rounds fly through the wall. He fired back just as the ringing stopped and everything was dead silent. As Gramps and others stuck their heads curiously by the door they could see the dust settle and saw that it was cleared. The blast had apparently killed all the men in the hallway and taken out the MG nest. Gramps was the first one out and searched the area. He walked to the end of the hallway and came back.

"Cleared!" Gramps yelled in Russian.

As the rest of them made their way to the hallway the gunfire outside the building continued. The mortars had stop but the battle was still very active and showed no signs of lightening up. As they walked up to the top floor to inspect the MG-42 machine gun position the gunfire down on the ground floor suddenly stopped. They all stood there frozen as they glanced grimly at each other.

"Are you there comrades?" Alexi asked in Russian.

His answer was in the form of bullets that flew their way. They jumped back a bit and Gramps nearly fell over because he lost his footing.

"Natalia feed me!" Gramps said. He pointed to the MG-42.

"Yes!" She answered and began to put in a fresh ammunition belt from the can next to the gun.

Gramps got on the MG-42 and immediately saw about 10 Germans inside on the ground floor and more coming in. He immediately let the gun rip open and boy did that gun sing! Everything seemed to once again go in slow motion. He could hear every round that he fired and see where they implanted the Germans. He also could see the blood as it slowly gushed out after impact. After the last German went down everything returned back to normal speed.

"Holy shit! You mowed them all down!" Alexi exclaimed and laughed.

"Yeah. Now let's get the hell outta here!" He panted.

They nodded and they walked out of the building as a couple of men carried the wounded soldier one arm on each shoulder. As they got outside on the street a medic took him and they never saw him again.

Chapter 18

Berlin and The Bloody End

As the battle waged on and heavy street fighting continued many Germans surrendered to the Soviets. Some were lined up and shot while the lucky ones were sent to the back and viewed as less than nothing. The German POWs would be sent to salve labor camps notorious for harsh living conditions know as Gulags. There in a twist of fate the Germans would be subjected to the same hellish conditions that they had put the Jews and others through. The only difference was there were no gas chambers and it was a hell of a lot colder.

The group linked up with more of their men and engaged the Germans in fighting street for street building for building. It was real intense as the Germans fired Panzerschrecks, the German bazooka at them. They in return used an ant-tank rifle the PTRS-41 and stuck a scope on it to take out enemy troops. The gun was so powerful that even at a distance it still blew a good size hole in a person. If hit in the head from a distance or a direct hit from point blank range it was like shooting a chicken with a modern day Desert Eagle, it exploded. They charged against German troops that looked like young boys younger than 14.

The group set the wolves free and they charged with their owners, mauling their targets. Gramps unleashed the Samurai sword that he got from the Imperial Japanese in Bataan. The charge was like the battles of Feudal Japan or Medieval time in Japan. Gramps after his love of watching Samurai movie began to live it for he now was a real life Samurai. The last time a sword was ever used in combat in Europe was the First World War (1914-1918). However, since the advancement of vehicles and tanks Cavalry on

horseback was no longer needed. As they charged at them he could see the white of their eyes as he slashed them to bits. Blood gushed out of their bodies with every slash and it truly was worthy of a Quentin Tarantino flick.
It truly was chaos with gunfire ripping all around, grenades going off everywhere and airplanes doing strafing runs. The wolves barking and tearing through the Germans like steak. The screams and blood oh yes it was hell! Hand to hand combat began and soldiers used everything from the butts of their guns, to their helmets and fists. Gramps used his sword, knife and pistols. He also used his martial art moves to disarm and kill the Germans. Kicks, blocks, punches, flips and everything else you can thing of he did.
As German troops surrounded him Gramps quickly took care of them. He slashed the throat of one with his sword. Blood squirted out of the wound as the German held his throat with his hand before slowly crumpling to the ground, choking on his own blood. He swung and spun around slicing the Germans in the gut and chest. He put his sword back on his hip, pulled his pistol and fired. He kicked a charging enemy in the nuts. The enemy soldier bent over Gramps did a kick forcing his neck up and breaking it. He went down dead. Another one Gramps kicked him in the knee, grabbed him and used him as a human shield as his men fired, killing their buddy. He then threw down the lifeless body and kneecapped another one while at the same time shot two incoming soldiers dead. He then finished off the guy with a punch to the gut and a horizontal Judo chop to the juggler. He slumped to his knees and fell over dead.
As Gramps looked in the distance Anna, Natalia, and Alexi along with other Soviets were fending off wave after wave of troops. As Alexi threw a Molotov cocktail and as it exploded igniting the troops on fire they still showed on chance of lightening up. Scores of them charged at them while he continued to do hand to hand combat and fire with pistols. Now, in combat your sense of time is shot because what may seem like an eternity in reality was like ten minutes. However, in their case it truly was hours that they fought street to street and cleared building after building. They set up machine guns on the top floors and roof tops of building. They also deployed snipers in various tactical areas of the city.
As they set up camp for the night in a recently liberated house Marko now a Lieutenant Colonel let their men loose on their newly occupied area.

The Soviet Commander like other Red Army officers let their men loose and they committed many war crimes in the process. The men raped, pillaged and killed civilians by the droves. They did in a similar fashion what the Germans had done and the Imperial Japanese did in the Pacific. Alexi didn't like what was going on but he dared not to defy his brother, at least not in front of the other men. They celebrated their success so far by drinking vintage German wine that one of the men "liberated" for a nearby home. They also had sausages and a variety of meats courtesy of Marko who along with five others "liberated" a nearby butcher shop. Gramps didn't know it at the time but according to Alexi, Marko and the five other troops stormed the shop and killed the butcher and his family of seven who were hiding in the shop.

As Red Army soldiers rummaged and pillaged buildings and homes they recovered many treasures that the Germans had stolen from areas all over Europe. These discoveries would continue to occur even after the Germans surrendered. Artworks, books, precious metals and stones were found that night. It truly was a King's ransom and it wasn't even close to what they would soon uncover. Now, don't get me wrong Gramps has never accepted the men raping and looting personal belongings of Germans but he was all right with them taking their treasure troves.

The reason why was because these treasure troves were made up of items that the Germans plundered themselves so Gramps had absolutely no problem taking what wasn't theirs in the first place. The only exception that he had was if the Germans who owned the property were alive and by that he didn't mean that he would kill them just to get it. That was where he drew the line he also made it a point to inform the men under his command and gave them explicit instructions that if he ever saw or heard them committing such atrocities he would have them shot on the spot. However, Marko pulled rank over Gramps and instructed a "no see no hear rule" which basically was if they never saw it nor heard it then it didn't happen. Gramps was furious but then again it was Marko of all people and he really didn't want to get on the wrong side of that homicidal maniac.

After dinner and some drinking they slept on the floors, beds and couches of the house. They raided the linen closet and found an assortment of pillows. Needless, to say they slept quite comfortably that night. However, just before he fell asleep Gramps couldn't help but think that before this is all over it will go very wrong first. In early May his gut feeling would come true and it would have devastating consequences that no one ever saw coming.

Gramps led a group of soldiers into an apartment building to clear it when they were suddenly ambushed by no less than forty Germans. Gramps used his martial skills to take them out in the narrow halls. Exhausted, they staggered outside and were met with heavy Panzerschrek and automatic gunfire. The shoulder fired rockets completely wiped out the first floor as Ka'iulani and Gramps dove out the open window at the very last second. None of the men that he led into the building survived the intense rocket fire. Alexi, Natalia and Anna were with Marko battling it out extremely intensely one street over. They ran into a small number of troops but when they thought they had won a reinforcement platoon of SS troops and a unit of tanks suddenly came to the rescue. They wiped off the SS troops, took control of one tank and destroyed the other tanks with it.

Gramps managed to grab the STG-44 from the soldier that Ka'iulani attacked and mowed them all down.

"Mahalo sweetheart," Gramps said. He petted her head and scratched behind her ears.

Ka'iulani smiled and licked his other hand as he continued to pet her. After that Gramps linked back up with the gang as they swept the street.

"Where is the rest of the men? Marko asked. He looked at them.

"You're lookin' at it," Gramps replied. He pulled his canteen and sat down on the ground.

"That bad, huh?" Alexi implied.

"Does it need saying?" Gramps asked with a heavy sigh.

"Glad you made it," Natalia said. She and Anna hugged him and Ka'iulani.

"Of course I made a promise to my girls didn't I? And I always keep my promises, no matter what," Gramps replied with a smile.

They nodded.

As Anna, Natalia and Gramps climbed onto the tank Alexi and their wolves piled in jeeps behind them. Marko was in a jeep in front of the tanks and began to go.

"To the Chancellery!" Marko yelled. He floored the gas pedal of his jeep. All of them yelled in unison and steamed rolled to Hitler's headquarters.

The Reichstag building or the Parliament building was being taken by the Third Shock Army of the 1st Belorussian Front. They were responsible for the famous picture of hoisting Soviet Victory Banner Flag on the building. The act had occurred on April 30th but the famous shot wasn't taken until May 2nd when they had taken complete control over the building. That shot took its place as one of the most famous flag raising photos of the war. The other famous flag shot was of U.S. Marines hoisting the U.S. Flag on Mount Suribachi, Iwo Jima in the Pacific.

Back here in Berlin Marko got out of his jeep and stormed the Chancellery building. Natalia and Gramps were ordered to guard the streets and kill any Germans that were flushed out by their men. Both of them angry that they couldn't take part in storming Hitler's HQ nevertheless obeyed their orders pissed and under strong protest.

"Why the hell do they get to have all the fuckin' fun!" Natalia grumbled angrily.

"Yeah no shit," Gramps remarked.

Gramps spotted three SS soldiers, took aim and fired his STG-44. Natalia took aim at another one this time it was an officer with her Mosin-Nagant.

His eyes became wide and he hoped his reflexes were fast enough.

"NOO!" Gramps screamed and shoved her rifle down. She let one round loose.

The SS officer ran, dragging a large wooden crate got hit with the round in the leg and went down. Though from a far distance he recognized the face and it was one Gramps never could forget.

"WHAT THE HELL KEN!" Natalia screamed. Gramps sprinted to the wounded man.

Natalia ran behind Gramps and got the wounded soldier. The soldier was sitting down on the ground and bleeding a bit. He sat down beside him, pulled out a cloth from his pocket and handed it to the wounded soldier.

"So how you doin' Georgie boy?" Gramps remarked in English with a grin.

"Thanks. Eh the usual. You?" George replied with a British accent. He tied the cloth around his wound.

"George this is Lieutenant Natalia," Gramps said. He introduced them.

As George and Natalia's eyes met for the first time there was this instant spark. Natalia bent down so their faces were eye level with each other and they locked eyes.

"Wow Ken she's-" Natalia cut him off mid-sentence

"As are you," Natalia finished in English.

"Um might I suggest we take this somewhere I don't know- with some cover!?" Gramps remarked. He fired on a squad of Wehrmacht (regular German Army).

Gramps emptied his mag so he ejected it and replaced it with a full one.

"Yeah sure Ken as long as this beauty comes with us," George said still locking eyes with Natalia.

"Of course I'm coming with you," Natalia said softly and bent down to pick him up.

She swung her rifle over her shoulder and swung his arm over her shoulder. George picked up his MP-40 and hopped along with eyes still locked in Natalia. Gramps continued to blast at Wehrmacht soldiers and dragged the crate. The trio ducked into a nearby building and they waited for their men to come out of the Chancellery. Gramps examined and patched up George's wound which was thankfully a through and through.

"Georgie you mid tellin' me what the hell is in the crate?" Gramps asked. He panted.

"Oh that. Yeah its treasure," he simply said with a chuckle.

Natalia and Gramps looked at each other then back at him.

"Hey if ya don't believe me pop the damn thing open," he replied with a sly grin.

Natalia bashed the cover open with the butt of her rifle and oh my, did the contents glimmer back in the sunlight.

"Holy shit!" Natalia and Gramps exclaimed.

"Wait a minute, is this the Amber Room?" Gramps asked, He looked at the Englishman.

"Yeah beautiful isn't?" George said with a laugh.

"This is not all of it is it?" Natalia asked wide eyed.

"No, no the rest of the Amber Room is on its way to an old friend in London," George said with a wink.

"Ah Winnie," Gramps said. He cleared his throat.

George nodded.

"So whose hoard was this?" Gramps asked. He put the gold back in the crate.

"Well I was a lackey for some big wig Nazi named Albert Speer. He instructed me to pack up this stuff and meet him at some farmhouse where other shit was stored. Then, that fuckin' wanker decided to hightail it outta here. And left me with his shit!" George explained. He took off his helmet.

"Ah and when you saw us you decided to get 'captured' with the treasures," Gramps said. He pieced it all together.

"Yep. Although you gotta admit these are some of the most evil motherfuckers to ever walk the earth but they sure got good taste. And I didn't expect to take a round," he remarked.

The three of them began to laugh hard.

As George and Natalia began to gaze into each other's eyes Gramps knew it was love at first sight. Or in their case bullet at first sight. Their faces got close, George tilted his head to the side and they had their first kiss. Their kiss was a long and passionate one at that. Gramps just sat there and smiled. He rummaged around the area which was what was left of a bar.

He found a bottle still intact behind the counter and pulled it out.

"I couldn't find any cups. Just like old time Georgie," Gramps said. He showed them the bottle.

"I never complain 'bout that brah," he said in a flawless Pidgin accent.

Gramps laughed.

"Eh not bad. He go," Gramps replied. He opened the bottle.

Gramps took one gulp and passed it to Natalia. She took one gulp and then passed it to George. After George took his gulp he passed it back to Gramps. They passed that bottle back and forth to each other until there was not a single drop left. As the hours passed they became very drunk and merry. Gramps supposed it could have been the alcohol or the love between the two of them but George proposed and Natalia accepted it. Yeah, he thought it was a little bit of both but hey who knows?

"Hey our men are coming out!" Gramps exclaimed. He looked through the window.

"Quickly hide the crate!" George yelled at them.

Natalia scrambled to find something and somewhere to hide the treasure crate. She pulled off one of the dirty sheet covering one of the intact tables and with Grandpa's help they dragged the crate behind the bar. As their men came in with Marko first they just got back into position with Natalia beside George and Gramps behind the bar opening up another bottle. All of a sudden everyone had their guns trained on George.

"No, no!" Natalia and Gramps exclaimed. They shielded him with their arms and bodies.

"He is with us," Natalia said in Russian.

"Who are you?" Marko said in Russian. He pulled out his pistol and cocked it.

"He's an old friend of mine who doesn't speak Russian," Gramps answered in Russian with a grin.

"Ah an American," Marko said in English with a thick Russian accent. He lowered his pistol.

"No, just a fellow by way of London," George replied in English with a grin.

"Well however the way you came let's celebrate!" Marko shouted with glee. He waved his pistol in the air.

Marko's finger was still on the trigger and so everyone ducked a bit when he waved it around.

"Celebrate!" Anna yelled in Russian.

The rest of the men lowered their weapons and began to smile and cheer.

"Hey! A toast of the good stuff to you all!" Gramps exclaimed. He held up a couple of unopened bottles.

The men cheered and they began to once again pass around bottles.

As they got tanked Natalia and Gramps introduced George to everyone. They recanted the story of how they met via bullet and Gramps introduced him to Anna.

"Ah I see you have been doing well for yourself huh, Ken?" he remarked. He let out a sly grin.

Natalia punched the Englishman in his arm hard and he winced in pain.

"Yeah, I'm doin' alright," Gramps replied with a smile.

"You know we should make the announcement of our engagement soon," George said. He rubbed his arm.

"How about you guys get married tomorrow?" Gramps jokingly remarked.

George looked at Natalia and then back at Anna and Gramps.

"You know that is not a bad idea," Natalia replied.

"Yeah I mean why the hell not?" George added.

"Ok guess we'll look for a priest and a church in the morning," Gramps said. He scratched his nose.

They all agreed and the girls along with the rest of their men slipped into a deep drunken sleep. Only George and Gramps were awake because of a little known fact that was only known to them that Gramps slipped knockout pills in the alcohol before they drank it. The SOE partners needed some alone time to talk one-on-one away from curious ears.

"All right what the latest?" Gramps asked. He pulled out his canteen.

"Well Roosevelt is dead and-"Gramps cut him off.

"Wait? What?!" The Japanese American exclaimed. He abruptly stopped drinking from his canteen.

"Yeah, didn't anyone tell you? The old man is dead," he said. He looked at Gramps puzzled.

It was a monumental punch to the gut to think that the man who believed in Gramps and who placed him on this incredible journey around the world was now interned in six feet under the ground.

"I think I need a drink," Gramps said. He grabbed a bottle.

"No! No! Not that one!" George exclaimed. He threw his hands in front of him.

Oh yeah mahalos," Gramps said. He set the bottle back down and pulled a fresh one.

"To Frank Roosevelt the man who I owe everything to," Gramps said. He held the open bottle up.

Gramps took a large gulp and passed it over to George.

"Here, here," he said. He held up the bottle.

He too took a large gulp down and set the bottle on the bar.

"Ahh. Damn this shit is good!" George remarked. He smacked his lips.

"Oh yeah. So, what do you know?" Gramps asked as he looked at him.

"Well since Ole Adolf wacked himself out fanatics became even more fanatical and off their rockers ever since you guys finished up at the Oder. It was around that time that most of the high brass decided to make their escape plans or last one if you will. I wasn't there when Hitler got married nor was I there when the happy couple offed themselves," George said. He pulled out a pack of smokes.

He pulled out one and offered Gramps the pack. Gramps brushed him off with his hand and pulled out a cigar.

"What about the forces that we have encountered?" Gramps asked. He pulled out his lighter.

Gramps lit George's cigarette first then lit his cigar. After that he flicked his lighter closed and placed it back into his pocket.

"Oh yes as you may be aware of the drafting age was lowered and at this point they call for ever able bodied male to take up arms. Hitler Youth and Volkssturm (national militia) are among the forces we are now fighting. Others include Wehrmacht and SS. Although, all four are made up of only young boys and old men," he continued. He inhaled and then exhaled a large gray cloud of smoke.

Gramps nodded.

"Yeah I noticed that. They are desperate and this is the last ditch effort. I heard from one of the men I took prisoner that Hitler gave a hold or die order, right?" Gramps said. He puffed out a large cloud of smoke.

Gramps had his cigar in his fingers and then grabbed the bottle. He took a large gulp of it then handed it to George.

"Yeah he gave the order. So what have you got?" he asked. He grabbed the bottle from him.

"None of them have ever suspected that I am a spy despite my background. Marko, the CO and Alexi's older brother has tried to turn me on several occasions," Gramps said. He placed the cigar back in between his lips.

"Do you think he is a player?" George asked. His tone became serious. He shook the ash off his cigarette.

"Yeah. I suspect strongly he is an NKVD agent operating under Stalin's orders. I once saw him late at night sending out coded messages via Morris Code. He is also an ultra fanatical Communist. And before you ask no, the girls aren't honeypots," Gramps said. He took another swing at the bottle.

"But are you absolutely sure?" he asked. He took the bottle from Grandpa's hand.

Their wolves got up and began to nudge at their hands so they put their tobacco sticks in the glass ash tray on the bar and began to pet them.

George still glared at Gramps.

"I'm positive without a shred of doubt that the girls are not intel agents,"
Gramps answered with much confidence.

This later proved to be wrong for Anna.

"All right, all right. I do have to ask though, what is up with the wolves?"
he inquired.

Gramps chucked.

"Oh that yeah it's a rather long story," Gramps replied. He rubbed his
eyes.

"Well, we got time," George said. He looked over the bar full of sleeping
soldiers.

Gramps chucked.

The duo chatted like old times until the sun came up. Besides feeding
each other intel they chatted about what they had been doing since they last
saw each other in London.

"There was another girl in Berlin," George reveled drunken.

"No!" Gramps exclaimed loudly drunken.

"Yes-an American named Bailey. Beautiful like an angel," he said and
laughed.

Gramps laughed with him loud and hard.

"So, where is this beauty now?" Gramps asked. He opened up a new
bottle and sent the cap airborne.

Gramps handed it to his British partner for the first drink.

"Thanks. She's uh back in the states. She was my American counterpart,"
he confessed and took a gulp.

"Bullshit! She was one of Donnie's girls?!" Gramps exclaimed. He
petted the wolves.

"Mmm yep. Now get this her father was a trench buddy of Donovan's
and that is how she got the gig. Her cover was that she was a uh Nazi
sympathizer whose family hailed from Munich. And that she went back the
Fatherlands to support the Nazis cause," George said. He handed Gramps
the bottle.

"Ah and you checked her out huh?" Gramps said with a grin. He threw
one back.

"Oh yeah. Thoroughly. Yeah we had fun every night," he bragged with a
bigger grin. He took the bottle from the envious Japanese American's hand.

"She was amazing?" Gramps asked with a laugh.

"Oh so much. With a million dollar smile and sultry voice, she turned heads wherever she went," he said. He threw one back.

They laughed hard. He handed Gramps the bottle.

"You got where she was from?" Gramps asked. He swished around the contents of the bottle.

"Yeah, California," he answered. He scratched behind the ears of two wolves.

"You thing you'll ever see her again?" Gramps asked. He looked at the bottle as he continued to swish it around.

"Don't know but then again you never know," he replied with a twinkle in his eye.

"I'll drink to that," Gramps said. He held up the bottle.

Two hours later the old friends were so drunk they staggered and could barely see anything straight.

"You think she's yours?" George asked drunken.

"Who? Anna? Yeah I think she is bud," Gramps replied drunken with a short laugh.

"I know you have been straight with her but how do you think she'll take to your real mission?" He asked.

Gramps stared at Anna who looked so much at peace sleeping. At that moment his mind raced. He had forgotten why he was truly out here with the Soviets. The mission he was charged with by Churchill was to spy on them. He quickly put those thoughts at ease by picturing life together with Anna. He would take her away from all the death and scorched earth of Europe and start a new life. Warm sunshine, rows of coconut trees, and endless stretches of that white soft sands of Kauai. Unfortunately and unbeknown, this would never come true and no matter how much he wished it to over the years. However, in a way Gramps was glad it didn't turn out because his life turned out quite well. He struggled to come to terms with it for years but eventually did, though never fully.

As people began to wake up the duo were out looking for food. It was quiet fun to do so incredibly drunk because it reminded them of all the fun times the pair of SOE agents had together. They began to laugh just out of the blue right around the time they found a little store. It was a bit bombed out by artillery but they managed to recover some good stuff. Still ripe and intact fruits, and some meats as well as some eggs were among the items they brought back to the bar.

After the group ate a hearty breakfast they moved out.

Chapter 19

Tragedy and Romance

Marko spotted an SS uniform thus the shooting and chase began. Gramps was towards the back but could clearly make out a figure darting pass the rubble of buildings. Many heavy blasts of gunfire they fired and not one round hit the SS soldier. Their chase ended to an old Catholic Church which to Grandpa's amazement was still standing and seemed untouched by the endless shelling.

"Come out you worthless scab!" Marko shouted in German. He and others fired many rounds shattering the church's windows.

As Gramps got closer Marko ordered the men to cease fire. Marko ordered two men to stand guard at the back door while be pulled out two German stick grenades. With the men covering the back he armed the grenades and threw them into the church. The grenades went off with a thunderous boom accompanied by huge clouds of smoke, splinters from the wooden pews and very loud screaming. He anticipated the enemy solider bolted threw the back door right where he was snatched. The men dragged the severely wounded enemy soldier back into the church.

"Ken hold my weapon while I deal with this scum," Marko ordered. Gramps grabbed his PPSH-41 and off Marko went into the church.

In full view of all of them Marko unholstered his revolver, pulled the hammer back with his thumb, with his finger in the trigger and pressed it against the soldier's forehead. The SS solider who looked no older than 12 was bleeding all over and was on his knees. He gripped a rosary in his hands and was praying in German. Just before Marko was going to fire there was a loud thud from inside the confession booth. The other two men bashed the doors of the confession booth with the butts of their guns. They pulled out three Germans civilians an old man, an old woman and a young woman from the two booths.

They screamed and begged on their knees to spare the life of the solider. As Gramps listened in he found out that the SS soldier was the man's son. The old man was the Priest and the other two were his wife and daughter.

"MARKO! DON'T FIRE!" Gramps yelled in Russian.

However Grandpa's words fell on deaf ears and in full view of the boy's family Marko fired, painting the walls of the church with the boy's brains. That single gunshot echoed and for a moment there was absolute silence. Then, the family of the boy sobbed loudly as they held the dead body of him in their arms. Marko holstered his pistol and the three men and proceeded to walk out of the church.

Gramps was steaming in anger and sprinted over to the church.

"Ken! Ken! Don't! Ah fuck!" George yelled.

"Ken!" Alexi yelled and ran after Gramps.

"Hey Ken thanks for holding my weapon." Marko said with a smile.

"What the fuck! I told you not to fire goddamn it!" Gramps screamed. He got in his commander's face or because of his height rather his chest.

Gramps struck Marko with the butt of his own weapon in his stomach and he fell to his knees. Then Gramps kicked him on the side of the head and he went down. The other two men began to charge at Gramps; he kneed one of them in the balls; the soldier fell over instantly the other Gramps kicked in the kneecap, cupped both of his hands and gave him an ear slap on both sides. The man fell down dead. Gramps raced over to the family who were still sobbing hysterically.

Gramps bend down and began to comfort the family in German. All of a sudden Gramps head a soft click and slowly turned around. Marko stood there clearly in pain, with his revolver out, finger on the trigger, hammer back and it was pointed directly at his face. Alexi chambered a round and raised his tommy towards his brother's head. Alexi slowly walked over to Grandpa's sides and faced his brother. Anna, Natalia, George and many of their men did the same. The rest stood behind Marko and with their weapons cocked and pointed at them. Their forces now divided nearly down the middle with twenty on one side and twenty five on another.

"Ho how about we settle this like men or are you afraid shrimp?! Marko yelled angrily in English.

"I ain't afraid of you! You big piece of shit!" Gramps angrily spat back.

"Then why don't you put your money where your mouth is and fight me! No interference one on one!" he challenged.

"Let's fuckin' do it!" Gramps yelled in agreement. He steamed.

After a tense standoff all the soldiers slowly lowered their weapon. Marko and Gramps took off their ammo belts and handed off all of their weapons. As some of the men loyal to Grandpa's side guarded the family the rest of them walked outside of the church to resolve this pickle. The men formed a large circle and with Marko and Gramps in the middle the fight was on. Now, Marko was more of a brawler with no form other than brunt force. However, what he did have on Gramps was about a foot in height, fifty pounds and big massive muscles that bulged out. What Gramps had working for him was his speed and form. He just prayed that it was enough.

Gramps had his hands up in front of his face and Marko charged at him like a bull. Gramps side stepped him and tripped him with his foot. Right after the giant Russian went down he swept the American off his feet and Gramps joined him on the ground. As they came to and jumped back on their feet they looked one another square in the eyes and both realized that this was not going to be the easy feat they thought it was. Gramps rushed him blowing punches at his body and Marko just stood there and laughed. He punched Gramps in the gut and he nearly crumpled to the ground.

Gramps kicked him in the knee and he went to the proposal pose. As Gramps went in for another kick this time to his head Marko caught his foot in midair. Gramps did a spin and kicked him in the head with his other foot thus freeing himself. Marko, dazed threw a barrage of punches, hitting mostly air but landed three on Gramps. Marko shook his head and was back in the fight. Then, all of a sudden the Russian pulled out a Stiletto knife that was concealed on his ankle.

Marko swung around the knife hoping to slice Gramps but he was faster and sidestepped him. Gramps, now behind him kicked him directly behind the knees. His legs buckled and he was down on his knees. Gramps went in the front to face Marko, grabbed the hand with the knife, twisted it and with him screaming until he let it out of his grip. As it fell to the ground Gramps kicked it over the side. He then elbowed him in the face and did a spinning kick to the side of his head. Marko face planted the Earth and it shook, literally.

As Gramps began to walk away he heard gasps and a loud click. Marko pulled a small pistol hidden on his lower back and with his finger on the trigger cocked it. Gramps, in lightning speed pulled a Shuriken (Ninja Star) concealed under his sleeve, spun on his heels and threw it at him. The razor sharp star implanted itself on the back of the hand with the gun which he dropped immediately. Gramps rushed him, kicked him in the balls full force, with cupped hands slapped both of his ears, and finally jumped in the air and punched as hard as he could in the face. The Soviet went down once again but this time he didn't get up. As Gramps walked away all of the spectators including the family of the slain SS soldier looked at him in awe with their mouths wide open.

"Now let's get the hell outta here," Gramps said panting.

"Da," Natalia and Anna replied still in shock.

"Yeah, whatever you say Ken," George said still in shock with his mouth wide open.

Gramps whistled and their wolves sprinted to him. He walked off and many others followed him. Sometime later Berlin fell to the Soviets and so the spoils began for many of their troops. For them there was no bottle of the good stuff being popped open. Nope, Marko wanted Grandpa's head and Alexi was trying to stop him. Marko had had his hand taken care of and was hell bent on putting Gramps in the ground. Anna, Natalia, George, and Gramps were in the house next door to Marko and Alexi who ordered that no one but them be inside to resolve the situation. It was late in the night and Gramps was half awake but he could hear both Alexi and Marko's voices. He couldn't make out the words but from the tone and level he knew it was pretty heated exchange. It was obviously about him and presumably Marko banged his fist on the table. It was followed by probably Alexi who banged his louder. Then after a few more shouts came the click of a luger and a single round fired from it. Gramps was just too damn tried to get up and see so he just closed his eyes and drifted off to sleep.

Besides if Marko had killed Alexi then Gramps was already dead so he was in a state between deep sleep and awake. He was able to still interpret the sounds around him but it would take a bit for his reflexes to kick into high gear. He slept with an STG-44 besides him and had a British Commando Dagger under his pillow. He was an expert in using it and was a dead shot if he needed to throw it. The other thing was that Marko was a right handed shooter and couldn't shoot worth a damn with his left so Gramps knew if he did try to shoot him the Russian would have to use a scoped rifle. A blade on though he could use but Gramps imagined he would be in excruciating pain though because of the wound. Nevertheless, if Gramps heard footsteps closing in on him he was ready.

The next morning Gramps awoke refreshed and to his surprise undisturbed. Another surprise to him, the whole house was a buzz.

"What's going on?" Gramps asked very groggy.

George now on crutches hobbled to him.

"Alexi and Marko got into a heated argument last night and Alexi shot him dead," George said quite grim.

"So, who head now?" Gramps asked. He wiped his eyes.

"As of right now you are the highest ranking officer to us," George said with a grin.

"What?" Gramps said surprised.

"However, Alexi has taken command," George replied. He took out his canteen.

"Good cause I don't want it," Gramps said still half awake and groaned.

George nodded and drank from his canteen.

"Yeah, he figured you didn't. Now come on and get dressed," he said. He put his canteen away.

"Why?" Gramps asked now awake.

"Cause the groom and his best man shouldn't miss his own wedding!" George answered with a laugh.

"Bullshit! You serious?" Gramps asked still stunned.

George nodded.

"Mahalos brah," Gramps said. He hugged his British buddy.

As Gramps got up and changed in the bathroom George began to become impatient.

"Hey on the double! The other couple are probably on their honeymoon by now!" he yelled.

"What other couple?" Gramps asked from inside the bathroom.

"Alexi and the Priest's daughter," he answered. He took out his silver flask and took a large gulp.

"Bullshit!" Gramps yelled. He emerged from the bathroom with a clean shave and a clean uniform.

"Shit! You're gonna be the cleanest lookin' mate over there! And how the hell did you manage to carry a clean spare uniform?!" he exclaimed. He looked at Gramps.

"You're not the only one with an ace up their sleeve," Gramps remarked with a sly grin.

"Yeah, yeah let's go!" he muttered.

When the duo got to the church Alexi and the priest's family were at the alter along with Natalia who was waiting for George. Anna stood by the priest along with all of their wolves Gramps kissed her on the lips and stood there as the nuptials began.

"I will conduct the services in my native tongue of German as it is a common language that we all full understand. Two couples married at the same time is quiet unheard of and under such extraordinary circumstances. My dear daughter Gretta and a Soviet Captain Alexi a most handsome young man. The other gracious couple to be wed; Captain Natalia of the Soviet Army and Major George of His Majesty's Army of Great Britain. I will make this a short service to not arouse suspicion. As well as us getting out of here alive, thank the lord," the priest said.

They all chucked at that last line. Gretta, the priest's daughter was a tall, skinny girl who looked no more than 20. She was flanked by her middle aged mother and wore a stunning traditional white wedding gown made of silk. The dress was probably her mother's as the rationing in the war had made luxuries like this extremely if not impossible to come by. When the old man asked for the rings Gramps was blank faced because he had received any rings. They called their wolves, Henry Morgan (HM) and Emilia. Fastened to their collars were the rings for each of the couples. That took Gramps by surprise because last he had seen none of the wolves including his had collars. It made him wonder how long he was out sleeping for all of this to have occurred? As the rings were exchanged with sweet words and kisses planted Gramps began to shed some tears. As Gramps looked around he became clear that there was not a single dry eye there.

"You know I wonder what our wedding would look like?" Anna whispered.

"Depends on the season I suppose," Gramps replied with a kiss.

Gramps was 19 and in love or at least what he though was love. The women of Europe were much different than that of Hawaii and he was very tangled up with that, the war, his duty, his secret duty and his heart. He was deeply conflicted and in too deep.

As the wedding ended Alexi and George chatted with the priest. He and his wife seemed over the moon hugging and kissing them both. It was a few days later when the priest and the family took off in a jeep did Gramps find out what they were talking about. When Alexi and George went to talk to the old man about doing a marriage ceremony the old man flipped out and was afraid that they would meet the same fate as his boy. Alexi was quite smitten by his daughter and Gramps supposed she was a bit as well. So, the deal was made that in offering to marry the two couples the family including his daughter who would now be married to Alexi granted safe passage out of Germany.

George made some calls and arranged safe passage papers which included a map detailing known movements till now and with the help of Alexi a jeep for transportation. The papers that George had given them were that they were a high priority and that they had 'valuable intelligence' of the Germans and Soviets. The instructions were that they be highly defended in case the Soviets attacked trying to get them. Also, no one try to obtain this 'valuable information' but General Eisenhower or General Patton. If for any reason anything would happen to them while in U.S. hands the perpetrators would have to answer personally to one of the fine Generals listed above. The old man, his wife and daughter would drive until they hit U.S. lines where they would be safe. They were also given weapons and a machine gun was mounted on the back of the jeep.

A couple of days later the group were told by Alexi to pack up because they were moving out to Prague, Czechoslovakia. So, with the city of Berlin in ruin they said goodbye to it as they placed it in their rear view mirror.

Gramps had not known at the time but he would be back in Berlin seven years later.

Chapter 20

Prague and The Cowboy General

As the group rolled to Prague they all felt ecstatic that they had toppled Berlin and the fact that they all had survived so much. The hellish winters, offensive after offensive, battle after battle, through everything by some miracle they had survived it all. Some of them as Gramps mentioned before had served in Stalingrad and to have survived everything until now was incredibly rare in itself. It was on that tank ride on a "liberated" German King Tiger that Gramps had thought about his journey from Kauai and how far he had come. He chuckled because it was an incredible feat too. As he reminisced of his long journey here he couldn't help but remember all the buddies that were killed or left behind along the way. All those times they laughed together, all those time they fended off the enemy and of course all the women that he had loved.

Upon his reflection Grandpa's noticed how beautiful the natural terrain was for the first time. All this time it had been cold, dark or blown up but the fields and hills were exceptionally gorgeous. As he pet his wolf and marveled at the scenery George tapped him on his shoulder.

"Hey you ever thought we'd end up here?" George asked with a smile.

"No, never," Gramps replied with a chuckle.

"Yeah neither did I," he said all smiles.

The group reached the Ore Mountains in the South and from there made the push into Prague. The Soviets and the U.S. military were putting immense pressure on the Hitlerites in Prague. They along with the U.S. surrounded the area from all sides. What was going on the Prague was to become known as the Prague Uprising. It was when the Prague Resistance and the German Army went head to head on May 5-8. While the uprising was in full swing the soviets launched the Prague Offensive on May 6. The uprising ended with a German victory but it was to be short lived for the Soviets were right on the verge of entering the city. On daybreak on May 9th Soviets entered the city of Prague. The group were met with some intense pockets of resistance but nothing they couldn't deal with. The offensive ended on May 11th. Prague was the last major operation the Soviets carried out during the War. It was also to go down in history as the last major battle of the European theater of World War II.

A few days prior on May 6th U.S. recon teams had gotten into Prague but were unable to help the resistance against the Germans due to some political bullshit with the Soviets. If Patton had used his forces to intervene the uprising would have easily been won by the resistance. However, that was not the case and with the news of Red Army troops the Czech people took to the streets in celebration. Marshal Ivan Konev head of the 1st Ukrainian Front received a warm welcome with loud cheers by the citizens of Prague.

Over the next two days the group met with General Patton's 3rd Army in various places. It wasn't until they met with Patton himself did they find out that the Germans surrendered unconditionally a few days earlier. While Alexi and Anna celebrated the victory and mingled with U.S. Troops Natalia, George and Gramps were meeting with Old Blood and Guts himself. The trio snuck away and met in the American General's tent. He was alone and greeted them warmly despite his well-known disdain for the Soviets. They sat down and they got to chatting. The first thing that caught Grandpa's eye was his famous Ivory handle revolves on his hips.

"Ah I see my revolvers have caught your eye, Kabazawa," Patton said. Gramps eyeballed the beautiful sidearms on his hips.

"Yes, sir they are quite a work of art," Gramps replied. He looked at him.

"Did you get my message, General?" George asked. He scratched his head.

"Yes, I did. Congratulations on your recent marriage, Major." he said with a smile.

"Thank you General," George replied with a smile.

"So what news do you folks bring?" he asked.

"Soviet forces have laid waste to Berlin looting, raping and killing every German in sight. Many art pieces and cultural artifacts from various countries will now end up in the hands of the Soviets as well as jewels and precious metals. However, they have also been looking for and rounding up any brains of the Germans. Scientists that worked on their rocket programs for example are prime targets. As well as the minds who worked on the super weapons programs for the Germans as well," George said without missing a beat.

"And Ike says we can trust the Russians," Patton scoffed. He rubbed his chin. "Excluding present company of course."

"Thank you General," Natalia said with a smile.

"What do you have Sergeant?" he asked. He turned his attention to Gramps.

"Sir?" Gramps asked puzzled.

"Well, that was your rank when you were in this man's army wasn't it, son?" he asked to Gramps.

"Yes, sir it was. I concur with the Major as I was present and have witnessed first-hand the savagery of both sides. Captain Natalia and I here were part of the force that liberated Auschwitz concentration camp. After that well we tended not to take any more Germans as prisoners," Gramps said. He rubbed his tired eyes.

"Well, hell I'm just stunned that you Reds took any at all!" he remarked with a laugh.

Then they all began to laugh at the comment.

"General did you by chance check under a sheet in the back of the jeep?" George asked.

"No, why?" he asked.

"The treasure that I spoke of earlier, sir? It's under that," he reveled. He let out a sly smile.

"Ah yes well I'll have a look at that later," he answered with a half grin.

"You loaded the treasure into that?" Gramps asked a bit surprised.

"Well, yeah I mean as much as I believe Alexi is a good guy I don't trust him with that," George replied.

"I'm sure you folks have heard the news over the German surrender?" he asked. He changed the subject.

George, Natalia, and Gramps looked at each other in surprise and then back at Patton.

"No, what news?" Gramps asked.

"A few days ago the German High Command surrendered unconditionally to the Allies. The war in Europe is over. They proclaimed the day, May 8 as V-E Day or Victory In Europe day," Patton said.

"Well, then lets crack this baby open," George remarked. He pulled out a large bottle from under his coat.

"Very nice. We'll do this soldier style. No cups. That is if everyone is all right with that?" Gramps asked. He looked around at the rest of them.

"Well, I have no problem drinking with a Soviet woman. Just don't tell a soul," Patten remarked with a smile.

They all nodded and George opened up the vintage 1890 bottle of red wine.

Two hours later they drank the botte dry.

"Well it's been swell General," George said with a smile.

"Yes, it has. Oh I almost forgot your wedding present," Patton said. He reached into his pocket and pulled out a large sealed white envelope.

He handed it off to George who opened it and scanned the document. His eyes grew bigger as he got the bottom of the hand written letter and inspected the other papers attached behind it.

"Havana, sir?" George asked. He looked at Patton in surprise.

"You earned it, Soldier. Sergeant, the latest intel report stated that you are to leave tonight via plane to meet with Stalin in Moscow. For a quick getaway Ike has sent a man with the instructions to fly you to Havana to join your friends. You'll need this," Patton said.

He pulled out another large white sealed envelope and handed it to Gramps. He opened it and scanned the document. Like the one he gave George it was a hand written letter from Patton authorizing Gramps as a VIP with no hassle from anyone and explicit instructions that he may board whatever to get to Havana, Cuba. The other attached papers were about the hotel, car, restaurants and attractions in Havana.

"Thank you, sir," the SOE agents said. They saluted him.

"No, thank you," he replied. He returned their salute.

After that the trio walked out of his tent and back to their tent. Patton would now play the role of peacekeeper between the Soviets and the Czech people. General George S. Patton died in a jeep accident in Germany in December 1945. He was 60 years old. By his request to lay with his men he was buried at the American Cemetery and Memorial in Hamm,

Luxembourg. Over 5,000 American KIA soldiers are there keeping him company for all eternity. The cemetery is fitting resting place for the spitfire General who loved his men right to the end and them to him. He, like many Generals of that era had a larger than life persona but was one of the few that despite it all still remained good men. Patton, was a spitfire and like a few others that Gramps knew lived for war. When the war was all but won they would not know what to do with themselves and so they would continue to look for someone else to fight. He never forgot the little guy and fought hard for the enlisted men. He was harsh to his officers because it was their job as such to see that the men under them have the essential supplies they need.

Alexi told him that there was an airplane standing by to fly Gramps to Moscow to meet with Stalin himself. It was to leave later that night. Natalia and George were also planning on leaving that night as well. Later that night Anna and Gramps sat under the starry night sky and marveled at it one more time. She begged the Japanese American to take her along to Moscow but Gramps had not told her that he didn't plan to stick around the Soviet capital though. The invitation was strictly for Gramps and Gramps alone so he confided in Alexi who offered to look after the wolves and Anna while he was gone. Gramps consulted George who tried to get Anna passage to Cuba but even with all of their connections sadly none beared any fruit.

Natalia told Alexi and Anna that she and George were going away for a bit but were planning on coming back. Natalia would take her wolf along with George and make their way back to Patton's camp where they would begin their Honeymoon festivities to Cuba.

"Will you come back for me?" Anna asked with tears rolling down her face.

"Yes, I will my love," Gramps said. He wiped away the tears and kissed her on the lips.

As Gramps boarded the unpressurized airplane he waved at Alexi and Anna who were on the ground with their wolves. Then he walked into the airplane and they took off. At this exact moment Natalia and George were digging out as well under the cover of his exit and most of their men were already all drunk from celebrating their victory.

That last conversation and sight of Anna is one that has haunted Grandpa for years and continued till the day he die. He hated himself for not taking her with him. They say it gets easier with time but it never did for him. On top of that she never told him he wasn't the only one keeping secrets. Some years later in another war he would finally find out the truth. He would be enraged but the truth is well the truth so he had to accept no matter how painful it was to accept.

Chapter 21

The Red Heart

In my Senior year of High school with pressure mounting for my Dad and school I fully gave into my addictions. I had given up on all the good things and just wallowed in grief over the loss of Grandpa. I was broken, sad, angry. I was a fuckin' mess.

Ones' senior year in high school is meant to be a time of reflection. It's the end of the public school years and usually time spent living with parents. Most will be going away solo to colleges and universities, military services and job positions away from the friends and family they have been brought up with. In my case I was reflecting on the one person who had been there with me for nearly my whole school life. He was also the one person who wasn't there physically to see it come to an end. The more I went to school, the more I was reminded of my Grandfather and I couldn't stand it any longer. So, came in three addictions into play.

I desperately needed an escape from this cycle of hell. Mostly I needed assurance that I was not alone and there were others who could relate but I'd take a temporary escape for now. It was then I remembered a story of how Gramps pulled of the greatest caper of all time. Before you ask no he didn't die in this one. Although, if he was caught he surely would have been.

Gramps didn't really remember much of the flight from Prague to Moscow. He slept much of the way. The only thing that he did remember was how damn cold it was in the airplane because it was unpressurized. Also, due to this his ears hurt a lot but he was just so exhausted he slept the entire way. The pilot respected him too much to wake him when they did pit stops here and there for fuel. So, he slept undisturbed until he awoke just as they landed in Moscow.

Once out of the plane and after exchanging salutes with the pilot Gramps was ushered by a private car to some grand hotel in town and he was shown to his room on the third floor. As soon as the hotel room door closed he dropped his stuff on the floor and took a nice, long, hot bath. When he emerged feeling all fresh and clean he noticed new clothes laid on the bed along with a note. The note stated that they were gifts from Stalin and that Gramps was to be ready for the car to pick him up at 9PM to head to Stalin's residence in Kuntsevo. There Gramps was told that Stalin was going to be home shortly and that he was free to look around. After looking around a bit Stalin arrived home and they ate dinner.

After dinner Stalin led Gramps to a room, opened the door, and they walked into his quarters. They talked about Grandpa's experiences though he left out a lot for security purposes. They drank and talked some more. When everyone was asleep they had some serious discussions. The Russian leader tried to turn him and buttered him up quite a bit to do so.

"You have done a fantastic job to the Motherland and as a reward for you exceptional service you are hereby promoted to the rank of Colonel. I will also give you a large house with lots of land and a posting of your choosing. I have also set up an account with one million inside as starter. However, I get a feeling you're not the type to be persuaded by monetary figures," Stalin said in Russian.

"And all you want in return is information?" Gramps asked in Russian. He slouched in his chair.

"Yes, for you already have proved your loyalty when you had ample opportunities to run away to U.S. and British lines," he replied. He stared right at Gramps.

"True. Thank you for being such a gracious host and I greatly appreciate the exceptional hospitality. As well as the incredible offer but as you have stated I am greatly loyal and that is not for sale period," Gramps stated. He tried his best not to show any emotion.

As Gramps declined the offer he tried to mask the nervousness of his voice and the immeasurable fear that he felt. He thought for sure he was going to be killed!! Gramps meant Stalin was a guy who sent millions of his own people to their deaths in slave labor camps, in battle and mass purges. And the worst thing was he never gave it a second though nor did he ever lose a second of sleep over it.

As he looked back on it now Gramps shouldn't have been too afraid for the Soviet leader needed the information in his head thus needed Gramps alive and in good shape. So, regardless of his answer he would have gotten out of his residence with his life.

Stalin shifted his weight in his chair and began to speak.

"Very well I greatly admire you undying loyalty to America but are they not the very ones who have rounded up and persecuted your people all for being Japanese?" he asked.

Gramps chuckled.

"You really must want me bad, huh?" Gramps countered and scratched his cheek.

"Yes, I do and I would never ever question your loyalty. Now, go back to your hotel and think about it, yes?" he replied with a grin.

Gramps nodded and Stalin yelled out a command to the guards outside of the room. They opened the door and walked in. Stalin and Gramps shook hands and he walked with the guards. They showed Gramps the door and the car came around to collect me. He was driven straight back to the hotel and escorted by the driver who was in a Red Army dress uniform and boasted a sidearm on his hip. After they got out of the car he popped the trunk, pulled out a submachine gun and slung it over his shoulder with the strap. As Gramps walked into the room he noticed that the driver was one of two soldiers who stood guarding the door to the room. The other soldier also donned an army dress uniform, boasted a sidearm (this time a revolver) on his hip and had a submachine gun.

"Spokoynoy nochi tovarishch. (Goodnight Comrade)," they both replied with grins.

"Da, spasibo moim brat'yam v dobroy nochi vooruzheniy. (Yes, thank you my brothers in arms goodnight)," Gramps replied. He shook their hands.

They all nodded and as they left the room to stand guard they closed the door behind them.

As much as Stalin 'trusted' him Gramps was restricted to his room and allowed out only to meet him. Over the next five days Gramps would order room service for breakfast and lunch with the evenings and dinner at Stalin's. After dinner at his residence he continued to try and turn him but Gramps wouldn't budge. The Soviet leader made Gramps a highly decorated solider with medals and awards as follows; Medal For Courage, Medal For Battle Merit, Medal For Victory Over Germany, Order of the Red Banner, Order of Suvorov, Order of Kutuzov, Order of the Red Star, Order of the Patriotic War, Order of Alexander Nevsky, Order of Bogdan Khmelnitsky, Order of Lenin, Order of Victory, and Hero of the Soviet Union. Gramps continued to also document his journey and everything that happened in great detail in his journal. Finally on the sixth day Gramps opened the up the cover of the room service cart, took out the bread and noticed something odd. Hidden in the bread there was a small glass tube, he took it out and noticed there was a note folded inside. He opened it up and read the note. The note was from Ike and as promised by Patton in Prague an American GI was standing by to whisk him away to Cuba.

The note also said that George and Natalia had made it safely and most importantly undetected by Stalin. That was a massive relief as Gramps had not heard nor did Stalin mention anything about them. The note instructed that an hour after it was to be delivered to him that he should make his way down to the kitchen were the GI was undercover. From there he would take him by car to where the airplane was and thus would begin the long flight to Havana.

What Gramps now had to figure out was how to take out his guards and slip away. He still had some knockout pills and a bottle of vodka; all he needed were some cups. He rummaged around the room and found three cups in the bathroom. He poured the vodka into the three glasses, crushed two pills into a fine power and dumped them into two of the cups. He sired them with his spoon until it was completely dissolved. Then, he finished his breakfast. After he was done eating he opened the door and offered a drink.

The Red Army soldiers graciously took it and they drank. After a few minutes they staggered and fell over out cold.

Gramps dragged their unconscious bodies into the room and tied them up with towels and sheets. He then packed up his stuff in his duffle bag and went down into the kitchen. He found the American GI or rather he found Gramps, the Americans drove to a small field where the airplane was and they high tailed it out of there. The GI was dressed in kitchen staff clothes. The plane was pressurized and Gramps slept without worry. They made a few fuel and food stops here and there although he didn't remember much of it as he was just usually half awake.

After I got home I looked up to see if there were any American GI's who served under both the Americans and Soviets. I plugged it into Google cause well they don't call us the Google Generation for nothing. Only one name came up Joseph 'Jumpin Joe' Beyrle. Joe served with the U.S. Army's 101st Airborne Division. He was captured a few days after his combat jump on June 6, 1944, D-Day in Normandy, France. In January 1945 he escaped a POW camp and ran into the approaching Soviets. From there he was fought with the 1st BN 1st Guards Tank. He was wounded in February 1945 and while in the hospital was visited by Soviet Field Marshal Georgy Zhukov. Zhukov very impressed with Beyrle's story gave him official documents to join back up with U.S. forces.

The more I read about Jumpin' Joe the more amazed I was.

Chapter 22

Under The Cuban Sun

When the American Spies landed in Havana, Cuba it was nighttime and all the stars were out in the sky. The warm summer breeze and the smell of salt air rushed blasted through Grandpa's body. He became very much awake by it as it felt like home. As they walked out of the airplane the pilot said that he was also to be his driver to the hotel. When they pulled to the hotel it was a beautiful sight and grand sight. The place Patton and Ike had put them up at was the Hotel Nacional de Cuba. It was an elegant place and as they walked in he saw the back of the head of an old buddy. The pilot whose name was Mark got a room on the second floor while Gramps got a room on the fourth floor.

"See you around Ken," Mark said. They shook hands at the front desk.

"Yeah see ya 'roud Mark," Gramps replied with a smile.

Mark walked off and Gramps went to visit and old friend. Natalia was talking with George and she saw Gramps but he waved her off to act normal. Gramps came up behind George and made his hand like a gun and jabbed it in the Englishman's back.

"Stick um' up brah," Gramps said with a smile.

George stopped talking mid-sentence and slowly turned around.

"Ken you bastard! You made it!" he exclaimed. They hugged each other.
"Of course I did. Sorry if I'm a bit late," Gramps replied all smile.
After George was finished Natalia and Gramps hugged and exchanged
kisses on the cheek.
"So what room are you up in?" Natalia asked excited.
"You tell me," Gramps replied. He handed her the hotel key.
"Ah! Just at the opposite end of the hall from us," Natalia exclaimed
giddy with glee.
"Well then let's go!" George remarked with a grin.
The trio went up to the rooms and after Gramps got settled he went to
George's room and knocked on the door.
"You guys ready for drinks?" Gramps posed.
"Oh, as always," George remarked with a sly grin.
They all chucked and went downstairs, jumped in their rental car and
drove to the bars.
After ordering drinks they began to catch up. They told Gramps about
how everything was so beautiful and how the weather was amazing.
"Oh and the beach! Oh such warm water! We have to take you!" Natalia
exclaimed.
Then their drinks came and it flowed like tap water for the rest of the
night. That night was the first time Gramps ever drank rum made in Cuba.
They drank various brands including Havana Club rum. It was here that he
developed a liking to it and aside from vodka and beer it took a place as a
favorite. While they drank and chatted the night away he noticed that there
were quite a few members of various branches of the Cuban military around
as well. They didn't seem to be interested in the trio but rather chatting with
their buds.
Cuba had declared war on the Axis shortly after Pearl Harbor was lit up
in December 1941. It was one of the first Latin American countries to do it.
They had U.S. weapons and gear courtesy of the U.S. Lend-Lease Program
which they benefited well from. By the end of the war they were one of the
best militaries in the Caribbean. There were quite a few U.S. servicemen as
well due to Guantanamo Bay Naval Base in Guantanamo. The other reason
was because of the Island's strategical importance to the U.S. They, much
like the Cubans didn't seem to mind them and so there was no trouble
between any of the trio.

This was the Cuba that generations had never got to experience. This was a time before the streets belted the songs and marches of revolution. It was before the Castro brothers led a successful communism revolt that overthrew the government and made the tiny island nation now a Soviet ally 90 miles from U.S. shores.

"You know we gotta take you shopping tomorrow," George said. He looked at Grandpa's clothes.

Gramps nodded.

Gramps didn't have many clothes that would suit him in the tropics and so the next day they went shopping.

The trio started out the day with breakfast and then went shopping. Gramps got another pair of dark Ray Ban sunglasses to replace the other one because the tint had nearly all come off. He also got many pairs of shorts both swimming and regular; a bunch of tee shirts, a few pairs of good dress pants, a couple dress shirts, two ties, another suit jacket, and a nice Fedora hat. They had tons of money from the back pay that George had received from the front desk the day he checked in. Gramps also later received his and returned the favor by fighting to pick up the tab wherever they went.

About a few days after the trio got back to the hotel from the beach a girl from George's past came into play.

"FUCK!" George whispered, stopped dead in his tracks and pulled Gramps aside hidden from view.

"What is it?" Gramps asked, puzzled.

You know Bailey the OSS girl from Berlin?" he asked nervously.

"Yeah-oh don't tell me," Gramps replied. He realized where this was going.

"Oh yeah she's just checking in at the front desk," he said. He motioned with his eyes and head to the front desk.

"Did she see us?" Gramps asked. He looked at George then at the front desk.

"No," he answered. He scratched his head.

"What are you takin' about?" Natalia said. She joined them from parking the car.

"Uh..," George and Gramps both said nervously.

"Come on dear what is it?" Natalia asked concerned.

"Ok I'll tell you but you have to promise not to lose your head," George stressed.

"You know babe you can tell me anything- What the hell are you talking about?!" she blurted loudly.

The men both shushed her and placed their hands over her mouth.

"The girl checking in at the front desk is an old flame of his from Berlin," Gramps blurted out.

"Oh. We should drop in on her and say hi," she replied. She pulled their hands off her mouth.

"No, no we really shouldn't," George and Gramps both exclaimed.

"Why not?" Natalia posed.

"Cause Bailey the girl, is OSS and if she catches that accent of yours she will think we've defected and are spying for the Russians," George answered. He gave in.

"Oh yeah that will definitely ruin our honeymoon for sure," Natalia remarked. She looked at them.

"Yeah so Ken I need you to do me a small favor," George said. He turned to Gramps.

"You want me to run interference don't ya?" Gramps asked. He massaged the back of his neck.

"Please and thank you. Or rather *Mahalo*," George buttered up with a smile.

"All right but you owe me," Gramps stated. He pointed his index finger at his buddy.

"Yeah, yeah I know. I just need you to keep her away from bumping into us," George instructed.

"With legs like that this should be a cakewalk. I wonder if the rest of her looks like?" Gramps remarked. He stared at Bailey.

"Ohh if you can get that far you're in for a treat," George said with a goofy grin.

"All right boys George and I better get out of here," Natalia suggested and shot the pair an annoyed look.

"Yeah go I got this," Gramps replied with a sly grin.

George nodded and the honeymooners made and break to the elevator while trying not to be spotted.

Gramps coolly walked right up alongside Bailey and began to speak.

He hadn't told George but Natalia knew that he had been easily picking up on Spanish.

Bailey was white or haole as we say in the islands, had long golden blonde hair, skinny fit frame, dark green eyes, and her skin was a tanned color. She was wearing white shorts that showed off her beautiful long tanned legs, dawned an ultra tight fitted striped top that made her figure look like a Greek Goddess. As for her feet she had on some killer heels. She stood at a tall six feet in height with the heels. She would stand at a short five foot six inches minus the heels. Just by the sight of her made men turn their heads. Yes, she was one of those, a showstopper.

"I'm so sorry Miss, but your room is not ready yet," the front desk lady said in Spanish.

"I was told it will be ready by now!" Bailey shouted in Spanish.

"Again my apologies. Would you please accept a complementary drink while you wait,

"Fine. Thank you," Bailey said enraged.

"Hola. (Hi.)" Gramps said in Spanish with a smile.

"Hola," Bailey, bitter replied in Spanish.

"Estoy Kinjiro y tu' eres? (I'm Kinjiro and you are?)" Gramps asked. He got his game on.

Then the OSS agent's face lit up like a Christmas tree and Gramps swore she began to talk Spanish a mile a minute.

"Whoa hold it!" Gramps exclaimed in English. He held up his hands.

"Oh, sorry I thought you were fluent," she replied.

"Yeah no not even close," he said with a smile.

They chuckled and laughed.

Oh her laugh it was something that you could lose yourself in!

"I'm Bailey," she said. She held out her hand.

"Kinjiro," Gramps replied. They shook hands.

"Yeah I got that part. So what bring you down here?" she asked.

"Funny I was just gonna ask you the same question," Gramps countered.

"Well I beat ya to it so spill," she said. She wore a seductive smile.

Bailey had this glint in her eye and along with that smile it nearly put Gramps over the edge. He began to let out this big grin. The next thing he remembered is he had her bags in his hand and was kissing her repeatedly as they made it to his room. They got in and he just threw down her bags on the floor, shut the door and they rolled all over the bed. I'll leave you to envision how he 'distracted' her.

You must understand back then the attitudes were that the whole world was at war and no one had a clue when it would be their last moments so people quit waiting and dove right in there.

Grandpa may have been extraordinary in a lot of areas but in other he was like any other 19 year old kid. He had eyes for the ladies and secret agent or not that was a hard thing to suppress.

After the war or at least the European theater was over, many civilians and war fighters rejoiced in well, does it need saying? Later once the war was complete over it resulted in the biggest birth rate increase ever. It was called the Baby Boom which began just as servicemen returned home from the war. Simply dubbed 'Boomers' this new generation of post war children would be born in 1946 till 1959 or 1964 in the U.S. In other countries the dates vary but nevertheless they all saw some spike in birth rates.

Bailey and Gramps went to the beach one day and splashed one another with water she screamed and squealed. She then splashed him with the water and she tried to run away but he chased her and grabbed her in his arms. She squealed and laughed as he held her in his arms. Bailey turned around and they kissed just as a wave splashed over them. After the long, gaze of the sunset they laid there on the beach under the cotton candy colored sky. The beach was secluded so they laid next to each other, silently in awe of the vibrant color of the sky.

Occasionally they would turn their eyes on each other and then they laid there in each other's arms. He stroked her arm with his fingers and felt the salt beginning to crystallize on her soft, tanned skin. Vibrant orange colors lingered in the sky while they just continued to sit there and watch the waves crash onshore. The breeze picked up the strong salt air and tickled his nose The strong salty air would trigger fragments of Kauai but after all he had been through his real home seemed so foreign. Sometime after nightfall they decided to go and head back to the hotel. When they got back Bailey undressed and took a bath. Gramps decided now was his chance to slip away and inform George and Natalia. He opened and closed the door slowly making sure that he didn't make a sound doing it.

Gramps knocked on their door and Natalia opened it. She then grabbed him, tossed him inside the room, poked her head out of the door and closed it. She then walked to towards him and called George over from the bedroom.

"Now, having fun are you?" George remarked. He took notice of the big goofy grin on Grandpa's face.

"Oh yeah," Gramps chuckled.

"Good now remember she is a highly trained operative. And aside from you she is the best I have ever encountered. So for the love of all that is good and holy be fuckin' careful!" George warned.

"You think she's still reporting to Donnie? And what the hell you think I am a goddamn amature!?" Gramps asked. He fired back.

"Can't say for sure cause remember only half of the war is over," he replied. He turned his head from side to side cracking his neck.

"Alexi said that tensions are mounting in Europe," Natalia injected and changed the subject.

"You called Alexi?! Are you trying to get us all killed honey?!" George vented. He turned to her.

"I was careful and as Ken here knows Alexi can be trusted despite what reservations you have 'bout him," Natalia fired back.

George sighed loudly and ran his fingers through his hair.

"All right, Tex has Bailey ever gone into her room alone?" George asked. He turned back to Gramps.

"No, not once. She's been in my room for the past three weeks. In fact this is the only time we've been apart," Gramps said. He picked up a nail file from the bed and began to file his finger nails.

"Okay. Go uh back to the room and just act normal. It looks like we're all gonna be here for a while," he said. He made his game plan.

Gramps nodded.

Gramps hugged Natalia and shook hands with George then began to make his way to the door.

"Hey you'll need this," George said. He tossed Gramps a book.

"Mahalo," Gramps replied. He looked at the book.

Gramps slipped back into his room unnoticed and laid on the bed. With the book in hand he looked at it and began to flip through it. The book was English to Spanish guide. So then he began to seriously to learn how to speak Spanish fluently. The bathroom door opened and a billow of steam rolled out. There in the fog like steam Bailey stood like a black silhouette of

Aphrodite, the Greek Goddess of Love. She wrapped herself with a towel giggled and walked right up to kiss the very smitten Japanese American. They kissed once more. He grabbed her and rolled over on the bed so now was on the bottom and he was on top.

"My turn," Gramps said softly. He got off the bed.

He walked to the bathroom and took a bath. By the time he got out she was fast asleep still only wrapped in air on the bed. He fully clothed, lifted her up and placed her under the covers. Bailey slept in the nude regularly and he didn't have any complaints about that whatsoever. He may have been gentle but he was still a man after all. As George put it he was a rather cheeky bugger. He guessed the drive and their activities had sadly done her in.

Gramps and Bailey continued their romantic relationship for months and every once in a while he would slip away and report to George and Natalia. George let Gramps borrow the car but because Bailey had a rental too they used hers mostly. The Americans took turns driving as they explored all of Cuba in the time they were there. They were always in each other's arms and it was like a dream. Aside from spying on each other if there was anything better than this Gramps didn't wanna hear about it. He meant think about you and a girl after adventuring all day, sitting on the beach arm in arm just the two of you with a bottle of the good stuff, watching the sunset. After the sunset you and her still lay out on the beach with a bonfire roaring under the stars. Come on! Don't tell me that's not every guy's dream right there!

Anyway Gramps collected wood to build a bonfire Bails got out chocolate, graham crackers, and some marshmallows. By the time he started the fire she had already found a clean stick to use for the marshmallows. He lit the wood and the blaze began. S'mores was on the menu tonight for they already had dinner and lots of rum. They roasted them to a slight char on the outside and sandwich the gooey marshmallow in between the chocolate and crackers. The first one he did he left it too long and when Gramps pulled it out it was on fire. Bails laughed and did hers perfectly. So, needless to say she was better at it than he was.

Bails sat in his lap with her head under his chin and they just laughed under the starry night sky. There they were under the stars with the sound of the ocean, the crackle of the fire and her beautiful voice. Yes, life was good, it truly was great. Later she fell asleep on his chest and he never dared move because he was in pure nirvana. Bails looked like an angel when she sleeps but when she began snores oh, boy it sounded like a sailor! As she slept he slowly began to pull out his English to Spanish language book and read it. He took it everywhere with him and made damn sure he kept it hidden from her.

As the weeks began to turn into months Gramps realized that in the process of playing he was in love with her he had fallen deeply and madly in love with a girl. It was later that he explained to me that he had begun spying too early and as a teen he couldn't separate himself from one area, Women. Bails was beautiful, smart, funny and everything you wanted in a girl regardless of what generation you lived in. He believed that she was genuinely falling in love with him as well. He would later learn that she was playing him too but eventually had fallen for the dashing kid from Hawaii.

She often talked about her plans after the war was completely over. Her younger sister had married the son of a furniture store owner and her older brother was off fighting the Japanese in the Army. To make matters worse her mother had pressured her to marry because they were desperate to have grandkids.

One late night she told him of such a guy whom she had been with.

"I was engaged once, you know. His name was Tom and he was beautiful. He was big, strong as an ox and had a good heart. Tom was four years old than I and he joined the Army right out of high school. He became a pilot in the Army Air Corps. He proposed just before he volunteered to fly with the Brits in 1940. He was killed in the Battle of Britain," Bails reveled to Gramps one night.

"I am so sorry Bails," Gramps said. He held her tightly in his arms.

"Yeah so am I," she replied. She kissed him.

It was on these nights that she opened herself up he did too. In the process he found out that she was born and raised in Southern California and thus learned Spanish from a young age. Her parents divorced when she was ten. She lived with her mother in California while her father moved to his hometown of Littleton, Colorado. She, her brother, and younger sister would visit him along with their mother every summer. In the winter her father would come and spend the holidays with them. The reason why they split was merely just that the romantic spark had fizzled out. They got along together great with no problems and remained the best of friends. Nor her father nor her mother ever remarried.

Gramps opened up and spoke about how he and friends mischievously had stolen watermelons from a watermelon patch while pretending to look for a down bird they shot using a BB gun. He told her of Kauai and its valleys, hiking trails, beaches, wildlife, plants and of course food. He also told of the history and people. With each word her eyes widened and she hung on every word. She liked most was the tales of his family and the legends of the islands.

"You know you should be a writer," Bailey remarked one night.

"Me? A writer?" Gramps said as a joke, baffled.

"Yeah, cause I just close my eyes and I can taste the food on my tongue or see the breathtaking views of – that trail you mentioned," she said with confidence.

"The Kalalau Trail," he said.

She nodded.

"Perhaps later when this war is over," he replied with a half grin.

"Good and when it comes out I want a sighed copy," Bails remarked. She pointed at him with her index finger.

"You got it darling," he said. He kissed her on the lips.

Gramps and Bails "talked" for hours with such passion and fire. He could still smell the sweet perfume Bails wore. They just laid on their side gazing into each other's eyes and grinning about the future they envisioned. A future they would never have.

The couple also made other trips to the beach and Gramps armed with a spear, two sets of diving goggles, and a bag for the catch. He and Bails swam pass some of the most beautiful and colorful fish he had ever seen. Big fish and little ones alike it was beautiful and so was she. As they swam around they marveled at all they saw and at each other. When they got back to shore he swept her right off her feet and spun around on the shore as they looked at each other and laughed. They made another bonfire that night and cooked the catch of several fish. After removing the scales, organs and such he sharpened some sticks and put the fish on skewers over the fire. He slightly turned them until the fresh catch were completely cooked and then they ate.

Then like all good things the ride came to an end. On one August day there was a massive commotion in the streets and when Gramps asked what was going on it changed his life.

"The American dropped some kind of super bomb on Japan," a Cuban soldier said in Spanish.

"A super bomb?" Gramps asked in Spanish still puzzled.

"Yes, one that destroyed an entire city," he replied with glee.

"What?! My god. Thank you for the information," Gramps shocked answered.

The Cuban soldier nodded and went on his way.

"Bails, is that possible?" Gramps asked. He turned to her mortified.

"I-I don't know," she stammered.

The bomb that President Harry S. Truman had dropped on the Japanese city of Hiroshima was the world's first atomic bomb. The atom bomb or atomic was named "Little Boy" and on August 6th and it was exploded midair. It resulted in the deaths of over 200,000 people many of which were civilians. Truman gave the Japanese time to think and surrender after the bombing. However, they refused and another bomb called "Fat Man" was dropped on the city of Nagasaki three days later. Another 100,000 people again mainly civilians were killed for the world's second atomic bomb. The bombs had the destructive power of 15 kilotons and 20 kilotons of TNT. The bombs set off and with the help of the wind spread radiation in the air. This is what thousands ended up dying from, radiation poisoning. This was the beginning of the atomic age.

In November 2013 7 years after Gramps told the story of learning of Hiroshima being nuked I was touring the Hiroshima Atomic Bomb Museum in the Peace Memorial Park in Japan. I glanced over the pictures of the destruction and death that the bomb did. It brought me back to that 11 year old kid hearing about it for the very first time. Grandpa visited Hiroshima in 1952. He got choked up when he described what he saw there. It one of the only times I ever asked him if he was okay. He would nod silently and continue his story. He never went to Nagasaki. After what he saw in Hiroshima he had expressed no desire whatsoever to go there. By then he was a two war veteran and after witnessing so much death and agony I believe it was just too much for him to handle. I would go back again to Hiroshima on a family vacation in the Fall of 2017.

On August 9th the Soviets declared war on Japan and with the help of Mongolia invaded Manchuria and Korea. With the pressure mounting the Japanese finally agreed to the terms of unconditional surrender which was announced on the radio on August 15. The speech was made by none other than Emperor Hirohito himself. The world rejoiced while in Japan massive rioting occurred. The Emperor and his family had to be evacuated for safety. The Emperor in Japan at the time was considered a God on Earth and to lead his people to victory always. This proved that he was not a God and so many angry people took to kill him. In Japan at the time because of the war there was a shortage of essentials such as food and many were just scraping by. The country was on the verge of poverty and once the war was over it was on the brink of civil war.

The project which the bombs were developed was called the Manhattan Project and it was the United States' first Nuclear weapons program. The project had been started by President Roosevelt in 1942. The products of the top secret project were tested at the Los Alamos Laboratory in New Mexico. To this day the facility continues to develop and study weapons of which include biological, chemical, and nerve agents. They also work in technological fields of things such as nanotechnology, renewable energy, medicine, supercomputing and advancements in space exploration.

Three days after the announcement of Japan's surrender or V-J Day (Victory Over Japan Day) Gramps got a phone call form General Douglas MacArthur himself and he asked if the 19 year old Japanese American wanted to be there in person when the Allies conduct the formal surrender ceremony.

"I thank you greatly General but Truman cheated and I may get shot there," Gramps replied. Anger set into his tone.

"I understand son. Thank you for everything you have done to the service of this country and the preservation of the world. I look forward to one day meeting you in person for this country owes you, I owe you a great debt. And please call me Mac you've earned it," he commended with a chuckle.

"Thank you, sir- Mac. Hmm Big Mac, how is that, sir?" Gramps asked.

"Sound good. Sound good Ken. Until we meet in person Happy VJ Day Soldier," he said.

"Happy VJ Day Big Mac," Gramps replied.

After that the phone line clicked and he hung up. Gramps just stood there frozen as he still held the phone next to his ear. He was in great shock or shook as we say now over the news of Japan's surrender and news of two entire cities being flattened by one bomb each.

It was a surreal experience that the war that ravaged the entire would and had resulted in the deaths of millions was finally over. The war had reshaped the world and would go down as the bloodiest conflict in the history of the world. Gramps had witnessed first-hand the brutality of men and women from many nations on both sides as well as the bloody conclusion of the Eastern European Theater. As Bails and Gramps kissed and broke open a bottle of the good stuff to celebrate they talked about their post-war plans. Bails had always loved horses and when he told her about the horses he had back on Kauai she was ecstatic. Her plan was to buy a large plot of land in San Diego where she was from or in Littleton where her father was. There she would live on a farm with some dogs and a bunch of horses.

"To live in peace after all of this seems like a good idea," Gramps remarked with a smile.

"Yeah, it truly does," Bails replied with a chuckle.

Chapter 23

Journey Home

Four days before Japan's September 2nd surrender signing on the deck of the USS Missouri in Tokyo Harbor a loud knock came on the door. Gramps opened it and standing there were three U.S. Army soldiers. With the sight of the soldiers there he had flashbacks to when his house was ransacked by army troops just a few years earlier. They advised them that Bails and Gramps would be going home via U.S. Army transport plane later that night. They were also sworn to secrecy over their wartime activities and that they couldn't tell another soul what they had done for a period no less than 50 years. As he closed the door Bailey sat there on the bed in silence. The soldiers visited George and Natalia next but he could hear them Bails couldn't. She was in shock of it all he guessed. The war being over and now they were going home. He guessed like him even though they talked about home they never had really thought about it. It was finally over. How were they going to come to terms with all they had done and seen? Also, how were they going to tell their families about it?

Gramps could hear that the soldiers told the exact same thing as they had told him except that since they were married they would be going to George's home in London. He was happy for them but fearful that they would meet at the airfield and all hell would break lose. Much to Grandpa's relief when the time came Bails was going home first and himself an hour later. He still remembered her face as she stood there with her bag in hand just about to board the plane. The scene was much like the end scene from Casablanca the classic movie.

"Come with me," she breathlessly whispered in his ear.

"I'm sorry. I can't, "he softly whispered back.

The couple kissed passionately one last time and he inhaled her perfume. It was a sweet smell of fresh spring flowers and vanilla. He handed her the last bottle of rum that they had drank and it was still half full. Whenever he close his eyes and think of her Gramps can still smell that perfume.

"We'll always have Havana," she remarked. Her lips made a seductive smile.

"Yes," he chuckled. "We'll always have Havana."

She laughed and nodded.

They hugged tightly one last time and he ran his fingers through her long hair.

"I promise we'll see each other again in this life or the next," Gramps said. he wiped the tears from her face.

"Until then see you later darling. I love you," she said. She looked into his eyes over once more.

"See you later my love, always," Gramps said. He gazed deeply into those beautiful eyes once more.

Gramps was sure gonna miss that dame.

After that she walked off and climbed aboard the plane. At the top of the stairs of the plane she looked back at him. Their eyes met one last time and as they waved goodbye part of him wanted to run up those steps and join her. It took everything in him not do just that. He had been in too deep and desperately wanted to hop on that plane with her. He had forgotten a major lesson of his training never think ally means friend. However, Gramps had the fear of how the hell he was to come clean with her or should he at all?

That fear he supposed was the one thing about her he truly and terribly regret. Although, it did work out best for both of them and like Anna he wasn't the only one with secrets. He still couldn't help to ponder what might have been.

Some years after his passing I heard Camila Cabello's Havana. The song was an international smash hit. It projected the memories of Gramps having the time of his life with Bailey in Havana. I could picture it like scenes of a movie with the song playing the background. I was pretty confident if he was alive and had heard the song it too would stir those memories of a long passed era in a Caribbean city with a girl and the amazing adventure they shared together.

As Gramps went back to his hotel room with a heavy heart, all the little pleasures suddenly looked how he felt gloomy and down. Hell, as he stared off into the night sky even the stars seemed duller! He wanted company and so knocked on George's room door. Natalia answered it and he walked into the room. There in the room they were packing up and as usual downing a large bottle of alcohol as well. Gramps sat on the bed as they packed up and George stopped for a moment and sat down next to him.

"Here. You look like shit," George remarked. He handed Gramps a glass of rum.

"Yeah I look the way you feel," Gramps replied. He threw the drink down the hatch.

"Why would I feel like shit? I got the girl," he teased trying to cheer Gramps up.

"Yeah, yeah. Fuck you!" Gramps said feeling better.

They laughed.

"Yeah well while you were off doing romantic antics Winnie called. He wanted to talk about Operation Unthinkable," he said. He took large gulps straight from the bottle.

"What is it?" Gramps intrigued asked.

"It's a plan that was drawn up towards the end of the war in Europe. A plan called for a massive surprise attack on the Soviets by a combined force of Americans and British. On the conditions that if the Soviets were to either pair up with the Japanese, prolonging the war. And / or if they refused to give up lands once occupied by the Germans that were agreed upon at the peace talks," he said. He drank straight from the chilled bottle.

"So what does this have to do with us?" Gramps asked. He took a sip from his glass.

"Simple our knowledge of the Soviet military, man power, morale, equipment, and insight on the players," he stated without missing a beat.

"One massive war ends and he wants to start another? Jesus Christ!" Gramps exclaimed. He took a large gulp of his drink.

"Yeah, well you know how he feels about the Russians no offence dear," he remarked. He took another large gulp from the bottle.

"Wait did you guys know about the plan for the U.S. invasion of Mainland Japan too?" I interrupted.

"No, we didn't know nothin' from the Japanese or American side. And beside we couldn't do shit anyway. I was the only one who had been in the Pacific. I could perhaps have run interferences between American and Japanese forces but that would mean exposing my identity. Had the Soviets also jumped in on the invasion I could possibly been there to run interference between all three nations. Stalin would have my head though, for flying the coup on him. But again, me being this huge secret it's kinda doubtful I would have been called. The Japanese thought I had died in Denmark and I was in the wind to the Soviets. Aside from that I couldn't have any knowledge that could have been useful. I didn't know the lay of the land cause I had never been to Japan. I knew how they thought and what they believed in but had no idea of the poverty conditions that they lived under in 1945. Most still fiercely believed in the Emperor. Had I or American intel known about that they would have realized it might have been possible to spark a civil war. It would have been done by providing food and supplies to resistance groups in Japan who wanted to end the war without other nations invading them. Those resistance groups would then attack the Imperials and begin a civil war. It probably wouldn't have gone on long for two reasons the poverty conditions and U.S. air support. However, the sheer will of those still willing to fight for the Imperials would be strong. Either which way the corpse count would be high. It was when the first occupation troops landed did they find the civilians making bows, arrows, spears and lances mostly out of wood," Grandpa said.

"So, how do you uh- feel 'bout going home?" Gramps asked. He changed the subject.

"Well, I can't wait for Mum to meet Nat," George said with a smile.

Natalia stopped packing for a moment and sat on the bed between the two SOE partners. George handed her the bottle and she took a large gulp from it.

"I am looking forward to meeting your family," Natalia said. He handed the bottle back to George.

"How do you think you Mum will take it?" Gramps asked. He yawned.

"I think she'll be over the moon," he replied. He tried to mask the nervousness in his face but Gramps caught it in his eyes.

"Now that it's all over you think you'll stay in the service?" Gramps asked. He took another sip from his glass.

"Hell no!" he exclaimed. He scratched his chin.

"So what then?" Gramps asked.

"Uh- I think I'll be a teacher. Yeah that sounds good," he answered with a grin.

"You ? A teacher? Oh God help us!" Gramps joked. He rolled his eyes.

"Shut up!" he said. He pushed Gramps playfully.

The trio all had a good laugh at that one.

"No but seriously I have thought about it and a teacher seems like a fit. I mean hell, what better way to share our knowledge and prevent another war like this one than to educate the minds of tomorrow," he stated. He took out a stick of gum and popped it in his mouth.

"Fuck that! You should run for Prime Minister!" Gramps remarked. He put his arm over the Englishman's shoulder.

"Me? Prime Minister? Hell no! I'd shoot my opposition! But seriously I think I'll retire somewhere warm like uh Bolivia far away from the drums of war. What are you gonna do?" he answered with a short laugh.

'Plan A is to retire in South America and plan B is to become a teacher, hmm,' Gramps though in his head.

"You know I uh- just wanna go home and ride my horse. Yeah and try to get back into all the things I did before this whole fuckin' war began," Gramps answered. Reality began to sink in.

George nodded.

"You fear you'll go home and both it and you will be unrecognizable," he remarked sympathetic.

"Yes, I do cause I don't know how to tell this story. You know all of what we had seen and done. And I just don't wanna have all of this to go untold and simply die with me. No way, fuck that!" Gramps dished out.

George and Natalia nodded.

Gramps was quite glad and relieved that he and George were in the same boat in terms of going home. He meant they all did things and saw things that few would ever understand. He supposed he was glad that he just wasn't alone with his fear.

"Well we leave for London at 11," Natalia stated. She attempted to brighten their moods.

"I leave a half hour after you," Gramps replied.

"Well, then let's not have this good bottle go to waste then," George remarked. He held the bottle up.

"Here, here," Gramps said in better spirits.

They chatted a bit more then just as they drank the bottle it was time for Gramps to bid them farewell.

"Hey whatever happened to the small chest of Amber Room Gold that was in the first crate we opened?" Gramps asked. He remembered.

"Oh, that? It went straight it Winnie by way of my cousin a Canadian Lieutenant who stormed Juno Beach. It was split into three parts between Patton, him and me. All of it. My share has been sent home mislabeled of course," George said with a sly grin.

"Oh okay," Gramps replied and smiled.

The trio walked out, drove to the airfield where a military transport was and Gramps petted Emilia, Natalia's wolf one last time. The Japanese American exchanged hugs and kisses with Natalia and hugs with George.

"Oh I almost forgot, here," George said. He handed Gramps an unopened bottle of Havana made rum.

"Mahalo my brother," Gramps said. They hugged once more.

"Mahalo for all of the adventures and great times. Aloha my brother," George said with a smile.

"I'll see you both later," Gramps said. He waved.

"See you later," they replied and waved.

The trio waved one last time as they were at the top of the steps of the airplane.

After they had gone Gramps went back to his hotel room and packed. He pulled out a bottle of rum and began to neck it. It didn't occur to him then that he might have been addicted to alcohol. He meant everyone drank for every occasion because they never knew when death would come for them. He saw it as normal constantly having a drink. It seemed like he was on autopilot drinking, packing everything away in suitcases and a duffel bag. He also found his papers for his own rental car that he didn't use. He finished the entire bottle and packing with ten minutes to spare. He went down to the front desk and gave back his key then, he was off the airfield. As he walked onto the plane it was silent and he just dropped his stuff, plopped down and went to sleep.

Gramps knew they made a few stops but everything was oblivious to be because sometime when he was sleeping all the memories of his journey since the Japanese attack on Pearl Harbor in 1941 till now had hit him all at once. All the memories and all the emotions had flooded back like a tsunami crushing and drowning him. He began to cry from all the friends he had lost as he saw their faces, remembered what they did together and hearing their voices. He was sad, alone, and afraid of what he what and how he was going to face his family when he got home.

Years after I reflected on these thoughts of Grandpa's life through World War II made me think about my life. For the first time I was no longer blinded by grief or addictions and could see clearly. I thought about the happy, sad, and miserable times. I thought about all those people, especially girls I had met through my life and all the missed opportunities with them. I don't have regrets over what I did nor the many missed chances. Why? Simple mentally I wasn't ready for anything. My only regret is the heavy price I had to pay for this clarity.

It was a blur when Gramps got home but he did remember telling his mother in particular all of what had happened to him since he had left in early 1942. He remembered that they had hugged tightly and cried many a river over it. She never brought up anything about it after that night as she knew how much of a painful subject it was to do so.

As for the rest of his family his brothers had some questions and Gramps answered them to the best of his ability. He tried all his might to not let his emotions get in the way but he usually was unsuccessful in doing so. Like with his mother after that night they never brought it up ever again. As he went back to his job working with cows at the Waimea Dairy he just couldn't shake the feeling that his journey was far from over. He meant he had started out as a brash 15 year old youth, who wanted to prove himself and had come back a hardened, rugged, 19 year old man. It would be five years later in 1950 that the uneasy feeling would turn into a reality.

Grandpa was now a deterrent or the plan b in case the United States would go on a head to head war with the Soviets. The world was changing with the end of the shaky partnership between democracy and communism. The stage was being set for a different kind of war. In any case it was anticipated that in the event of such a war the Reds would most likely invade Hawaii rather than bomb it. Hawaii was a location much too important to just flatten out. In any case he would be reprising his role as the man on the inside, funneling out information.

In the dead of night when everyone was fast asleep Gramps would sneak outside and stand under the night sky. He especially liked when it was a clear night because he could see all the stars light up the dark sky. He would stare at all those stars and that crescent shaped mood for hours and he would have many flashbacks. He would see his time in the Philippines where he met with Virgilio, the commander of a band of Guerrilla fighters. Through those nights in Casablanca and Copenhagen. Then all those various places on the Eastern Front with the Soviets, he continued to flashback. Finally, on the beaches of Cuba where Spanish music could be faintly heard. He would see all the faces of all the men and women that he had spent time with and grown to love all under that beautiful bright and starry sky. As he thought about them all and recalled their faces it saddened him greatly. Many of the girls whom had captured his heart during those few years he knew that he would never see them ever again. And as you will find out he was mostly right with a few exceptions that surprised the hell out of him!

About The Author

Born and raised on the island of Kaua'i in Hawaii Kyle Kiyotsuka has been mesmerized by stories all his life. When he's not writing he's hiking up the mountains, soaking up the sunshine at the beach, catching a movie at the local theaters or when he's not home on Kauai, traveling around. He's currently working on several different books, including the part two to this one. You can keep up with him on Twitter: @KiyotsukO and on Instagram: @kiyotsukoo.

Made in the USA
Monee, IL
17 July 2021